BY G. D. YARNOLD

The Spiritual Crisis of The Scientific Age

THE MOVING IMAGE

SCIENCE AND RELIGION
TIME AND ETERNITY

—————

G. D. YARNOLD

London

GEORGE ALLEN & UNWIN LTD
RUSKIN HOUSE MUSEUM STREET

PRINTED IN GREAT BRITAIN
in 11 point Baskerville
BY UNWIN BROTHERS LTD
WOKING AND LONDON

complex of ideas which these contrasted pairs of words call to mind. And here a quite remarkable consensus of opinion between the philosophy of the ancient world and the newer ways of thinking of the modern sciences offers a valuable clue, which, though by no means original, I have tried to follow through consistently. Time and eternity are concepts given to us in their relatedness: they belong to the structure of reality as it is apprehended by the human mind. The two contrasted elements of that *datum*, as observed, are persistence and change; and change is perceived only in relation to that which does not change. Consequently, to specify either is to abstract one element from a richer whole. In the attempt to characterize, while avoiding over-precise definition, I have been content to take time and eternity as symbols respectively of the changing and the non-changing. In terms of the distinction so made, it is possible then to isolate that characteristic of personal life which provides us with the sense of time as a fiduciary system for the ordering of those experiences which we call temporal. Thereafter, I have taken a new look at the debate between those who regard this world-order as the creation of purposeful divinity and those who would place the emphasis entirely on the evolutionary view of cosmic and organic process; suggesting that a new unity can be brought into our thinking by a proper attention to the temporal-eternal distinction. Finally, I have examined certain questions of a specifically theological nature which arise when we try to express biblical insights in the categories of modern thought: the personal responsibility of the individual, and the logic of history, in relation to the 'fore-knowledge' of God; the conditions under which particular revelation is possible, and what such revelation implies about the historical process; the doctrine of the Person of Christ, regarded as the participation of the Divine in the human, and of the Eternal in the temporal. This latter problem, by general consent, ranks as a crucial test of the adequacy of any theory of time and eternity; and leads quite naturally into a brief attempt to relate the temporal span of our own limited existence to the eschatological future opened up to the believer in Christ Jesus our Lord. (A fuller discussion of this question will be found in the paper I presented to the Third International Congress on N.T. Studies, to be published in *Texte und Untersuchungen*.)

My indebtedness to a number of authors will be evident from the footnotes. Others, to whom I owe much, are not always cited in the text; since what they have written has entered long ago into the general heritage of philosophical theology. Among these I would mention explicitly William Temple and A. E. Taylor, whose Giffords were almost definitive in their day; von Hügel, whose depth is scarcely plumbed even now; and F. W. Green, Fellow and Chaplain of Merton in my own day, who first excited my interest in this investigation by his use of the phrase *sub specie aeternitatis* in connection with the pilgrimage which led me from unbelief to faith, and from a scientific career to the ministry of the Church. Professor H. D. Lewis of King's College, London, has kindly read the manuscript; and I am indebted to him for a valuable discussion of some of the points I raised, though he is by no means committed to the view I have taken. Although many years in coming to the birth this book would probably not have been written at all except in the relative peace and quiet of an incumbency on the slopes of the Berwyn (ecclesiastical streamliners please note); and I therefore express my debt of gratitude to all who have contributed, wittingly or unwittingly, to its appearance—to my bishop; to my people; and not least to my wife, who has typed the manuscript, after enduring years of discussion.

Llanwddyn
October 1965

CONTENTS

PREFACE — *page* 7

I. *Time and Eternity* — 13

II. *The Biblical Language of Time* — 28

III. *Time and Change* — 41

IV. *Time's Arrow* — 56

V. *The Doctrine of Creation* — 76

VI. *The Christian and the Cosmos* — 90

VII. *Evolution and Christianity* — 106

VIII. *The Relativity of Time* — 123

IX. *Everlasting or Eternal?* — 139

X. *Eternity and Creation* — 153

XI. *Fore-knowledge and Freedom* — 168

XII. *Revelation of the Eternal* — 187

XIII. *Time and the Eternal Word* — 204

XIV. *Epilogue: An End of Time* — 220

INDEX OF PROPER NAMES — 227

INDEX OF SUBJECTS — 229

I

TIME AND ETERNITY

No philosopher, no theologian, can get very far without abstract nouns. Yet there is nothing harder to define, nothing further removed from our everyday living, nothing better calculated to puzzle the plain man. And most of us are plain men at heart, preferring to be left to occupy ourselves in our day-to-day experience without being asked to examine that experience at all critically. Even such a simple statement as this, however, immediately introduces another abstract noun. What is 'experience'? I know what it is to experience various things: joy and sadness (there we go again), 'the slings and arrows of outrageous fortune', a tooth-ache, a twenty-mile walk over the hills, and so on. The verb 'experience' presents no serious problems, but the noun is less easy to define. Generally it is an aid to clear talking and clear thinking if we resolve to avoid abstract nouns and content ourselves with saying what we experience, what we do, how we feel: in other words to confine ourselves to the kind of statement which is as little as possible removed from what we know immediately through the senses. The effort, though distinctly worthwhile, is never entirely successful. The abstract has a habit of cropping up in the most unexpected places if we let ourselves talk at all.

The word 'time' is one of the most notorious abstract nouns in the language: widely used in everyday speech, in science, in philosophy, in theology; but ill-defined in every context. What precisely does it mean? We know about sunrise and sunset; we know about clocks; there are twenty-four hours in a day, though it does not always seem so. It is four o'clock: time for a cup of tea. Eleven o'clock: still time to read another chapter before going to bed. The alarm goes off: time to get up. The word

drops off the tongue so easily; with a variety of shades of meaning, which we seldom examine at all critically. We use it when
something is required of us; when we ought to be up and
doing; when a friend who is expected for dinner should be here
but isn't. We admit that we are slaves of the clock; but excuse
ourselves by observing that civilized life would be impossible
if we were not. But what *is* time? Shrug it off with a '*mañana*' if
we choose. 'Procrastination is the thief of time'—two abstracts
in one short proverb—yet we have said something, and we
know we have said something. But still the question is there:
what *is* time?

If pressed, most people will answer in terms of the clock.
The clock ticks away at a steady rate. (What do we mean by
that? Never mind for the moment.) In effect we count the ticks
of the clock. That is a boring procedure though, and a great
waste of time. (It is something you can waste, is it?) So escape-
ments, gear-trains, a clock face, and moving hands have been
devised in order to save the trouble of counting the ticks. We
read off the time at a glance, having learned the trick before we
were five. Basically though, we are counting seconds, and there
are 86,400 of them between one midnight and the next—by
convention of course. It is all a matter of knowing how far we
have got through the day; what proportion of the day has
passed; how much is still to come. The units are arbitrary, in
the same way that units of length are arbitrary. Seconds could
be longer, if we had chosen to make them so: but then there
would be less of them in the day. The clock would have a longer
pendulum, and would tick more slowly: but the convention we
have works well enough, and we are used to it.

The second is arbitrary: but the day is apparently fixed. Let
us suppose though that the earth were to revolve more rapidly
on its axis. What would be the result on our time reckoning? If
we kept the same clocks, we should count less ticks from one
midnight to the next: and it would all be rather confusing
because different clocks would be affected differently. Nevertheless, we could alter the springs and pendulums so as to make
all our clocks keep in step with one another and with the
apparent movement of the sun. We could quickly adjust our
habits to the new conditions: but should we live longer?
Presumably we should live a greater number of days. And

similarly if we could imagine the earth to be speeded up in its orbit round the sun, we should presumably live for more years. But should we live *longer*? No, not at all. Nor, I think, would life seem any longer. The arbitrariness of our units of time is one thing: our sense of duration is another.

Perhaps we should not base too much on such an impossible and imaginary experiment as a tampering with the rate of the solar system: but one thing at least it does suggest is that we possess some basic sense of time, which is more fundamental even than clocks and the duration of the solar days. This inference at least appears to be legitimate. Is there such a thing as biological time, different from solar time? Or such a thing as psychological time, different from either of the former two? Different in what sense? In being faster or slower? This would not be a very satisfactory answer. We know what we mean when we say that a *clock* is faster or slower. It is a relative statement, implying the existence of some clock which is to be used as a standard of comparison, the clock kept by the Astronomer Royal for instance. But does it mean anything to say that time itself may be faster or slower? After all a clock is only a device for measuring time. A clock which runs faster or slower than the standard clock is simply a bad clock: it measures time incorrectly. The plain man in each of us will want to insist that there is such a thing as time; that we can measure it accurately or inaccurately, according as we use a good or a bad clock; and that time itself (whether solar, biological, or psychological) cannot be faster or slower in any meaningful sense. Time, he says, just goes its own way, independently of us all.

We have a hunch that time has an existence of its own, independent of clocks and solar systems; and yet that we ourselves have an inborn sense of time. Have we then something inside ourselves, some metabolic process perhaps, something which ages as we move on in life, which gives us an inherent sense of duration, or of the passage of time? In its present form the suggestion is somewhat confused: yet it contains, I believe, a germ of truth which we can explore later. It is not easy however to see that anything of the kind could give us all the same inherent *scale* of time. Perhaps that is why we find it convenient to use clocks and the apparent movement of the sun to provide a sort of 'public time', which we can all accept for social and scientific purposes. But the stubborn fact remains that we must all have some *sense* of time, which is given to us in the experience of being alive at all. To recognize this fundamental fact of human existence does not commit us to any theory whatever of the ontological status of time itself. Nor does it imply any prescribable mechanism by which our innate sense of time keeps pace with the entity which we call time. All that we admit is a phenomenon of consciousness, common to all men and paramount for the uncritical, by which we are aware of the passage of time independently of any time-measuring device. And to ram the point home, let us simply ask, Why do we make clocks? Or even sundials for that matter? Not surely so as to invent a new and mysterious thing called 'time', but in order to have an agreed standard by which we may talk about our temporal experience which as men we share. But if this is so, we are still no nearer to being able to say what time is.

What have the philosophers to say about it? Men have indeed puzzled and thought about the meaning of time at any rate since the fourth century BC. There is no agreed answer; but we can usefully take a look at some of the opinions that have been held. Plato[1] in a well-known passage speaks of God as making 'a kind of moving image of eternity; and while setting the heaven in order, he made an eternal image, moving according to number, an image of that eternity which abides in oneness. It is to this image that we have given the name of time.' This would seem to imply a qualitative difference between time and eternity, making the former dependent upon the latter. Time is thought of as a kind of copy of an eternal ideal; its movement signifying its very imperfection. But eternity is even more elusive a concept than time. As a definition Plato's words do not take us very far. Indeed it is arguable that they are intended less as a definition of time than as a statement of the contrast between the temporal and the eternal orders: the one imperfect and fleeting; the other perfect, permanent, and divine. Well known also among the ancients is the definition given by Aristotle[2]: 'we apprehend time only when we have marked motion, marking it by "before" and "after"; and it is only when we have perceived "before" and "after" in

---

[1] Plato, *Timaeus*, 37d.
[2] Aristotle, *Physica* (ed. W. D. Ross), Vol. II, Bk. IV, 219a.

motion that we say that time has elapsed'. Although not identified with 'motion' (the modern word would be 'change') time is seen as dependent upon 'motion'. For Aristotle time is that which can be numbered, or counted, in the movement from the earlier to the later. This implies an innate sense of before and after, which is to be rendered quantitative by numbering off, or counting, instants or intervals. Is this not a definition of a clock for measuring time, rather than a definition of time itself? Probably so; yet for practical purposes it is often convenient to think of time as being simply that which a properly constructed clock actually measures. This is an operational definition, adequate for scientific purposes, but not in any sense an answer to our deeper questions. It seems that for the ancient philosophers as for ourselves, time as a phenomenon of consciousness is logically prior to, and to be distinguished from, any measure by which it may be represented for public purposes.

The discursive Augustine, standing as he does in the tradition of Plato, is more concerned with the relation of time to eternity than with the nature of time itself. Kant is clear that we have a knowledge of time by intuition, in terms of which we are able to interpret our experience. He wrestles with the problems of the absolute nature of time, and its beginning if any; propounding a series of antinomies, which though generally agreed by philosophers somehow fail to resolve the elusive character of time itself. Indeed until we come to the modern scientific movement, and the need for precision in the understanding of time mathematically, not much more could be said than had been said already by the ancients. The physicists and mathematicians of the seventeenth and eighteenth centuries learned how to handle the notion of time, even though their work begs the ultimate questions, and is suspect from the point of view of pure philosophy. Newton's definition of absolute time is indeed nothing more than a precise working rule, which enables him to manipulate the equations of motion of the heavenly bodies: 'Absolute, true and mathematical time of itself, and from its own nature, flows equably without relation to anything external'. In fairness it should be added that this definition was intended to serve the limited purpose of distinguishing time from length and mass, and that Newton deliberately refrained from pursuing the deeper metaphysical questions. The form of

B

words which he adopted made possible the classical approach to the problems of mechanics, which is a veritable *tour de force*. Regarded as a definition of time in its ultimate nature, however, as it has sometimes been taken, it begs the fundamental questions. Time is made to appear as a kind of substance: it is endowed with the property of flowing: and its rate of flow is said to be constant. How can the rate of flow of anything be known apart from some device for measuring time? Small wonder that Einstein's re-writing of mechanics has involved the so-called relativity of time!

And so we come to the most modern school of philosophy, existentialism. Heidegger, any more than Plato or Aristotle, cannot be summed up in a few sentences: yet his great work *Sein und Zeit*, unfinished though it remains, is probably the most notable metaphysical break-through since the days of Greek philosophy. Heidegger[1] insists that *temporality* is 'the meaning of the Being of that entity which we call "Dasein" '. Temporality, rather than time, is the primordial state of being, or existence; for each one of us exists 'towards our end', which is death. 'Dasein exists as born; and, as born, it is already dying, in the sense of Being-towards-death'.[2] What Heidegger calls 'within-time-ness' is something given along with existence itself. Consequently we recognize the distinction between the 'now', and the 'then', and the 'on that former occasion'. In so far as a definition can be given in existential terms, this structure of datability stems from temporality and is itself time.[3] 'Temporality is the reason for the clock'[4]; and 'in a certain manner Dasein itself is the clock'.[5] Public time, according to Heidegger, the system of counting off in terms of the sun or an actual clock, remains completely undefined: the most that can be said is that 'if we are to cast any light on the genesis of the ordinary conception of time, we must take within-time-ness as our point of departure'.[6] The gist of the discussion, difficult though it is to follow in detail, is that the being of man is in essence something enclosed between two brackets: birth and death. It is both given, and passing away into nullity. All that we can mean by the word 'temporality' is given primordially

---

[1] M. Heidegger, *Being and Time* (tr. Macquarrie and Robinson), 38.
[2] *loc. cit.*, 426.   [3] *loc. cit.*, 461.   [4] *loc. cit.*, 466.
[5] *loc. cit.*, 469.   [6] *loc. cit.*, 472.

with human existence: indeed as existence. And from the fact that man is totally enclosed, so to speak, in a temporal mode of being, arises the consciousness of succession. In a general way, I believe, it would be fair to say that Heidegger's monumental study corroborates the view that the time-sense is a primary content of consciousness.

Probably the most we can say at this stage of the discussion is that our present existence is circumscribed in such a way that we are moving from a state when we were not to a state when we shall not be: at least so far as bodily existence goes. Within this circumscribed being we can distinguish before and after, the earlier and the later; which is at least an indication of what we have already called a sense of time. This innate sense of time, however, actually appears to tell us something more than the mere *order* in which events occur. It seems to involve some sort of quantitative measure (glimpsed though not numerically apprehended) of 'how long ago', which also is a given part of our human experience. Whether it can be said that this is time, or not, is a moot point. At least this primary experience of consciousness gives us the incentive to observe the sun's shadow or to make a clock. But we still can give no certain answer to the question, What is time?

WHAT ABOUT ETERNITY?

We have no direct experience of eternity in the sense that we have direct experience of time. This may, but need not, mean that eternity is different in kind from time. Philosophers and theologians have sometimes used the word eternity to indicate a time or duration of infinite extent, without beginning and without end; though the concept is by no means free from ambiguity, and has been subjected to devastating criticism. More commonly the word eternity has been used to denote a state of timelessness, something of a qualitatively different order from an expanse of time however long. After reviewing the many contributions to the discussion of the relation between time and eternity, J. S. Mackenzie[1] proposes a unified picture of reality in which 'process as a whole might be said to be eternal, though every particular part in it has a place in time'.

[1] J. S. Mackenzie, Art. *Eternity*, in *E.R.E.*

The eternal then 'includes the whole of time'. In his view 'time is simply the aspect of successiveness which the eternal process contains'. A not altogether dissimilar synthesis is advanced by A. P. Shepherd; whose title, 'The Eternity of Time', indicates the general trend of his thought. However, I believe it will be widely agreed that everlasting time and timelessness are such totally different conceptions that any attempt to *unite* them must be extremely hazardous. My purpose here is certainly nothing of the kind. I want to insist rather that in either sense of the word we ourselves in this life have no real experience of eternity. We live within time: indeed within a strictly limited period of time. And this means that eternity, in either sense of the word, is outside our grasp. We have, however, certain glimpses or intimations of a reality which we call eternal, and my question at present is, How can we best *conceive* the eternal? as everlasting in time, or as truly timeless?

The intimations of the eternal to which philosophers have commonly drawn attention are truth, beauty, and goodness. As abstracts these concepts must be approached with caution. Realities though they are by general consent, they must not be reified. We may call them qualities; qualities of propositions, of things, of actions: the important point is that they endure. There is a sense in which the truth of a proposition, the beauty of a thing, or the goodness of an act, endures beyond the moment in which the proposition is stated, the time in which the thing exists as a thing of beauty, or the moment in which the act is done. How can we best conceive this endurance?

Two plus two equals four. This is a proposition (definition if you prefer it) which is true now, which was true at all moments of past history, and which will always be true in the future. We may say that it is true at every conceivable moment throughout the time-series, however far the series may be extended backwards or forwards; or we may say that it is timelessly true. The latter seems to be the better way of putting it, for arithmetical truths have nothing whatever to do with time. They are simply true. Indeed in grasping any truth of mathematics or logic, whether simple or profound, we have formed a conception of something which is independent of time. If we speak of such truth as eternal we mean that it is timeless. In much the same way we recognize a timeless quality in a work of art which we greatly admire. Most works of art are indeed perishable: they endure as works of human creativeness only during a limited time. Yet within this limited period they have a quality which we rightly describe as timeless. Other forms of art, music for instance, may endure beyond the limits of perishable material: they can be performed or reproduced at any time, provided instruments can be found and players to read the score. Though not strictly timeless, we may so describe them without gross misuse of language. Where does all this point? To the fact that in experiencing beauty, even though it is presented to us under temporal forms which pass away, we catch a glimpse of something which is truly timeless, and in this sense eternal. Goodness also, in the sense of moral goodness, can be said to give us a glimpse of timeless reality. Being kind, being generous, being heroic (it is well to avoid the abstract nouns) are actions which, though remembered in time, partake of a timeless quality which enables us to glimpse the eternal.

When we say that truth, beauty, or goodness—or better, that which is true, beautiful, or good—has an eternal quality, we are saying something over and above the statement that these things are to be admired at all moments in the time-series, however it may be extended. We are saying that these things give us a glimpse of timeless reality: a reality which is the same at all times precisely because it does not itself partake of time. St Paul wrote, 'Whatsoever things are true . . . honest . . . just . . . pure . . . lovely . . . of good report; if there be any virtue, and if there be any praise, think on these things'. (Phil. iv. 8) Why? Because in a true sense these things bring our minds, temporally conditioned though they are, into contact with a reality which is eternal, timeless: and therefore into contact with him who is Eternal Truth, Eternal Beauty, Eternal Goodness.

By an exercise of the imagination we can indeed conceive time as extending further than any actual duration which we ever experience. We do this whenever we study history, or speak of the distant future. Even the idea of infinite time suggests something to our minds; though as every mathematician knows the concept of infinity is full of pitfalls for the unwary. The lay mind will insist on approaching the concept by thinking of a million years, ten million years, a hundred million . . . and will feel that even if this is not infinite yet it is not entirely misleading as a working conception of everlasting time. But the exercise reveals no resting place for those qualities which we glimpse as eternal. Occurring within time, and under temporal conditions, they seem to point beyond it. They seem to be intrusions into the temporal from another world. But though we can form a rough and ready idea of the meaning of everlasting time, no corresponding exercise of the imagination enables us to form any adequate picture of eternity in the sense of timelessness. Eternity is a mode of being of which we have no direct experience at all. The most we can do is to recognize a timeless quality, and then to postulate a state of being to which the truly timeless belongs.

Of the four words which make up the vocabulary of this discussion—temporal, time, eternal, eternity—three are given content directly in experience. The fourth, empty so far as experience takes us, completes the logic of the sequence. What time is to the temporal, eternity (the unknown) is to the eternal. How are we to use the word 'eternity'? The temptation is to pour too much into the word. Just as the incautious schoolboy wants to define a parallelogram as 'a quadrilateral in which opposite sides are parallel and equal in length, and opposite angles are equal'; instead of being content with saying 'a quadrilateral in which opposite sides are parallel'; so in defining eternity there is a temptation to specify a mode of being which is everlasting or timeless, unchanging and permanent, perfect and infinite. If we let ourselves say too much, what we say may all be deducible from one point (as in the case of the parallelogram)—or it may not. Caution and tidiness demand a one-point definition. To return then. What time is to the temporal, eternity is to the eternal. The temporal is that which passes away. Time is the mode of being of that which passes away. The eternal is that which endures, or which is timeless. Eternity therefore is the mode of being of that which is timeless.

If we are careful to use the word in this sense, we have the advantage of conciseness of definition; and by implication we have made a distinction between eternity itself and that being whose mode of existence is eternity. We are then at liberty to add that being which exists in eternity is permanent, perfect, infinite (if we find good reason for doing so) without committing ourselves to the statement that eternity itself is permanent, perfect, infinite—an addition to our definition which is not justified, and which is strictly devoid of meaning. Thus in philosophy as a whole eternity has been understood as timelessness; and the negative form of the definition arises from the fact that we can have no direct experience of this mode of being. We make the contrast with time simply by negating that which gives temporal existence its characteristic quality. But what is true of the philosophical tradition generally is by no means true of the language commonly employed for religious purposes.

THE LANGUAGE OF RELIGION

If the words 'eternal' and 'everlasting' are not exactly equivalent, at least first impressions suggest that they are used indiscriminately in religious contexts. Closer attention however discloses both an overlapping and a trend towards increased precision.

The Authorised Version employs both 'everlasting' and 'eternal' in the New Testament, but only 'everlasting' in the Old. The Revised Version continues to use 'everlasting' in the Old Testament quite uniformly, and 'eternal' almost invariably in the New.[1] A few examples will bring out the difference in flavour of the two versions of the New Testament. In John iii. 16 A.V. has, 'For God so loved the world, that he gave his only begotten Son, that whosoever believeth in him should not perish, but have everlasting life'. R.V. reads 'eternal life': and the Book of Common Prayer, following a translation earlier than A.V. in the 'Comfortable Words', of course retains 'everlasting life', which still remains therefore the more familiar rendering. In the discourse on the Bread of Life (John vi) we find in A.V. both, 'Whoso eateth my flesh, and drinketh my blood, hath eternal life' (vs. 54), and, 'Labour not for the meat which perisheth, but for that meat which endureth unto everlasting life' (vs. 27). The Greek in both cases is the same. On the other hand, where A.V. has, 'he that eateth of

---

[1] The principle of the Revisers was always to render the same word in Hebrew or Greek by the same word in English. The difference in the original language, together with modern philosophical usage, fully accounts for the language of R.V. A notable exception occurs in Jude 6, where R.V. has 'everlasting'.

this bread shall live for ever' (vs. 58), R.V. makes no change.[1]
In these respects the New English Bible follows the lead of the
Revised Version. 'Eternal' is used in preference to 'everlasting'
throughout the New Testament.

Here then are the broad facts of the use of 'everlasting' and
'eternal' in the English Versions. What is the general effect
upon the reader? I suppose the plain man is rather more at
home with the Authorized Version. He reads there of 'everlasting life', which he understands as life continuing for ever,
without end; and the occasional alternative, 'eternal life', he
naturally interprets in the same sense. The more sophisticated
reader however may well find himself more at home with the
Revised Version, or for that matter with the New English
Bible. In these versions he is free to give what sense he chooses
to 'eternal'; and having realised that in the Johannine writings,
eternal life is portrayed as a present possession of the believer,
he probably inclines to the sense 'timeless'. In other words, he
is very much aware of the difference in flavour between
'everlasting' and 'eternal'. Yet of course, throughout the New
Testament the Greek word is the same in every case. It is the
English vocabulary that introduces the variety. We have raised
here two entirely different questions. One relates to the way
in which the English Christian understands the words available
to him. The other concerns the actual meaning of the Greek
text.

The Book of Common Prayer uses the word 'eternal' very
sparingly indeed. It will be found for instance in the so-called
Athanasian Creed, for purposes of theological definition; but
hardly at all in the prayers.[2] The opening address of prayers
and collects may be, 'Almighty and everlasting God . . .' or
'Almighty and everliving God . . .'; but we should have to
look to more modern sources for any frequent use of, 'O
Eternal God . . .' Clearly English usage in this matter has
undergone some change in the past four hundred years. How
far does this reflect a change in theological thinking, or at least
in emphasis? Again the range of hymns in common use in
Christian worship employs both 'everlasting' and 'eternal'.

---

[1] The Greek, εἰς τὸν αἰῶνα, is close etymologically to αἰώνιος; but any phrase
using 'eternal' would be a clumsy alternative.

[2] Examples will be found in the Marriage and Burial services.

Once more the distinction between the plain man and the sophisticated worshipper appears to be valid. Watts' hymn, 'O God our help in ages past', contains both 'eternal' and 'everlasting'; yet the sense seems to be dictated by the lines, 'A thousand ages in thy sight are like an evening gone'. An old favourite such as this speaks to the plain man in terms he can understand, and presumably does much to form his idea of eternity. Whereas 'Eternal Ruler of the ceaseless round' can well express the more sophisticated worshipper's sense of timeless Reality upholding the created order.

Now although throughout the range of religious language the two words are never strictly synonymous, yet a case can be made for their approximate equivalence. That which is conceived as truly timeless *is* at all times, from the remotest past to the remotest future.[1] Even though God be thought of in terms of timeless reality, nevertheless he makes himself known to us in time, and his attributes are enduring in relation to the temporal order. Particularly in poetic expression, and of course religious language is always akin to poetry, his very timelessness can most readily be rendered in terms of figures drawn from the temporal order. In other words, whatever our theological conceptions may be, the plain man in each of us responds most powerfully and naturally to the pictures conveyed by the word 'everlasting'. Though we can go some way towards conceiving the eternal as timeless, we are none the less anchored firmly in time, and our thinking is normally conditioned by it.

Or, again we could make out a case for justifying the word 'everlasting' as an attribute of God on the lines of the treatment of religious language worked out by I. T. Ramsey[2] in terms of 'models' and 'qualifiers'. Then the word 'lasting' would be accepted as a suitable symbol to refer to God. This is the model. Various things last for a short time, a longer time, a very long time, or throughout historical human experience. To render

---

[1] Cf. Augustine. 'Nor dost Thou by time, precede time: else shouldest Thou not precede all times. But Thou precedest all things past, by the sublimity of an ever-present eternity; and surpassest all future because they are future, and when they come, they shall be past; *but Thou art the Same, and Thy years fail not.*' *Confessions*, Bk. XI, 13. (tr. Pusey)

[2] I. T. Ramsey, *Religious Language*. Ch. II. The word 'everlasting' is not in fact treated here: but a valuable discussion of 'eternal punishment' will be found in Chapter I of '*On being sure in Religion*', a somewhat similar case.

the model suitable for religious purposes we take the infinite jump implied by prefixing 'ever' to 'lasting'. Here 'ever' is the qualifier. And what Ramsey calls the 'queer placing' of the two words, to make 'everlasting', is at the same time a measure of the logical impropriety of the term, and of the need for discernment and commitment in the religious situation where the new word has currency. Thus we might say that 'everlasting' is a not altogether unsuitable word to use in a religious context with reference to that Reality which in more strictly theological language we describe as eternal in the sense of timeless. Be that as it may, our real job is not so much to justify particular words as legitimate alternatives in religious language. Indeed we are concerned less with the vocabulary of religion than with that of theology, though it is clear that the experience of the one must influence profoundly the terminology of the other. The real question at issue is whether at the intellectual level, and particularly in modern theology, eternity is to be conceived in terms of infinitely extended time or in terms of timelessness. This is a question where philosophy should be able to guide us.

Now in some theological quarters today there is a marked reluctance to employ philosophical categories at all. We are told that a profound difference of outlook existed between the Hebrew and the Greek minds; that the Church made a serious mistake when it insisted on pressing the truth of the Christian revelation into the mould of Greek philosophy; and that the results of that disaster are still too much with us today. Our job, we are told, is to get back behind the welter of patristic definition to the theology of the New Testament itself; there to breathe the fresh air of primitive Christianity; and in the process to resolve the formidable theological questions which rend the contemporary Church. Even if the aim is commendable, perhaps the programme is over drastic. True, the Hebrews learned to worship and to believe; but the Greeks certainly learned to think. And perhaps the contrast between the two races has been rather overdrawn. In spite of the great vogue of biblical theology, the value of which is certainly not to be denied, modern man is the inheritor of both the Hebrew and the Greek traditions. There would appear to be a place both for the believing person and for the questioning mind. This much at least we may concede: that in any philosophical formulation of theology, the philosophy must be subservient to the theology, and not *vice versa*. The substance of the Christian revelation was poured first into a Hebrew mould. If we, who are also heirs to the Greek tradition, are to give it adequate expression for our own understanding, we must bring the categories of philosophy into the service of theology. The Christian revelation dictates the facts: philosophy may provide the means of expression and formulation.

The immediate question we have to face then is this: Does the New Testament itself give us any guidance on the relationship of Time and Eternity in Christian thinking?

II

THE BIBLICAL LANGUAGE OF TIME

IT is maintained frequently that the biblical literature as a
whole points implicitly to a conception of time differing in
important respects from the philosophical or Greek conception.
Indeed not so long ago this idea was the hallmark of modernity.
The supposed contrast will become apparent as we proceed.
In so far as it expresses a true theological insight, and is not
merely the result of a more primitive intellectual approach,
it can be expected to be significant for a systematic study of
time and eternity in relation to the divine. It is by no means
easy however to reach certainty in this matter; particularly
in view of the fact that the distinctive biblical conception is
said to be inherent in the range of *words* by which time is
expressed. The words of long ago are slippery things to handle:
it is all too easy to read our own thoughts into them.

The two best-known studies of the subject proceed by
drawing a sharp contrast between pairs of words. Marsh[1]
emphasises the distinctive content of *kairos* and *chronos*, claiming
that their employment in Septuagint and New Testament
reflects underlying Hebrew concepts. Cullmann,[2] on the other
hand, constructs a biblical philosophy of time on the basis of a
distinction between *kairos* and *aiōn*; such that the Christ-event
becomes the mid-point of the time-line. Both of these well-
known studies, along with others in which similar lexical
techniques are adopted, have been radically criticised by Barr.[3]

The earlier conclusions of the biblical theologians have been
accorded such prominence that the general character of Barr's

---

[1] J. Marsh, Art. *Time*, in Richardson, *Theological Word Book of the Bible*; and
The Fulness of Time.

[2] O. Cullmann, *Christ and Time*, Eng. Trans., 3rd ed. (1962).

[3] J. Barr, *The Semantics of Biblical Language*; and *Biblical Words for Time*.

criticism may be indicated before we go into points of detail. He writes, 'We should do well to remember that we do no honour to the Bible by wringing from its words answers to questions which were not in fact in the minds of those who used these words, and that by so doing we may only obscure the undivided attention with which the biblical writers concentrated upon their own themes.'[1] The question at issue is the actual content of particular words; and it is implicit in Barr's approach that the *content* of a word must be sharply distinguished from the total meaning of the *context* in which it is used. Thus he questions the belief 'that the layout of the lexical stock of biblical Hebrew constitutes a reflection or adumbration of the theological thought of the Israelites, and thus ultimately of the actual theological realities acknowledged in that thought.[1] Bearing in mind the commonly held view that the Hebrew pattern of thought is imparted to biblical Greek, he therefore questions the thesis that individual Greek words become charged with essentially Hebrew conceptions, and consequently that 'general conclusions appear to emerge inevitably from the very fibre of New Testament language'.[2] This, according to Barr, is a position entirely untenable on linguistic grounds.

In view of this strong reaction, further examination is clearly necessary before any use can be made of the work of Marsh and Cullmann. Two distinct questions arise. How far are Barr's objections to lexical method justified? And, if these criticisms are accepted, does the whole idea of a biblical conception of time fall to the ground, or can it be shown to rest securely on other evidence?

MARSH—KAIROS AND CHRONOS

Without actually denying that the Hebrews had a sense of time as measured, Marsh maintains that the Bible always understands time 'realistically': that is to say in terms of that which happens in it, the opportunity it brings, or the fulfilment which it contains. 'Israel gave expression to certain convictions about the nature of the temporal process and the events that happened in it. We might . . . say that to the Hebrew mind time was not a chronological continuum but a theological

[1] *B.W.T.*, 14.   [2] *B.W.T.*, 18.

series.'[1] The contrast is therefore between 'realistic time', in which the Bible is supremely interested, and 'chronological time', acknowledged but of no great significance. The former, according to Marsh, is rendered in the New Testament by *kairos:* the latter by *chronos.* The importance of the distinction lies in the fact of God's control of history as distinct from nature. Thus to recognize the significance or content of a particular time is to apprehend the historical opportunity which God gives, and to respond to that opportunity. Marsh then observes the common use of the phrase 'at that time' (e.g. Deut. i.9) to refer back to the highly significant events of the Exodus, by which God called and constituted a people for himself.[2] By the time of Jeremiah it was possible to refer to the anticipated restoration and reconstitution of God's people by the same phrase, since theologically all history is of his making. 'If the prophet has really grasped the significance of the time of the Exodus, he will know what God is like and how he acts in history, and will be able to judge of the pattern of events in the near future, in so far as they embody the activity of God.'[3] In the Old Testament, it is suggested, 'that time' acquires an almost technical meaning: referring to one or other of the mighty acts of God, either the Exodus or the Messianic age.

It is with this background in mind that we are asked to observe the use of *kairos* in the New Testament. The ministry of Jesus opens with the proclamation that 'the time (*kairos*) is fulfilled.' (Mark i. 15) Thus we read, 'The time of Jesus is *kairos*—and so is a time of opportunity. To embrace the opportunity means salvation, to neglect it disaster.'[4] Further examples of the use of *kairos* follow, largely Pauline: e.g. 'now is the accepted time; behold, now is the day of salvation.' (2 Cor. vi. 2) The salvation offered in Christ is to be recognized as the content of this time. The Passion and Resurrection recall the Exodus and Deliverance of Israel. As the Old Israel was created at the one time, so the New Israel is created at the other. All the promises of God are fulfilled in the coming of Jesus Christ; and these facts serve to pour a wealth of meaning into the word *kairos,* so that whenever it is used 'some of these overtones can be heard.'[5] The position adopted by Marsh in

[1] *Fulness of Time*, 28.　[2] *loc. cit.*, 54.　[3] *loc. cit.*, 55　[4] *T.W.B.*, 262.　[5] *T.W.B.*, 263.

both his contributions may be summed up in his own words: 'The contrast between "chronological" and "realistic" (time) is exhibited in the N.T. distinction between *chronos* (measured time, duration) and *kairos* (time of opportunity and fulfilment).'[1]

Against this conclusion, and the kind of evidence on which it is put forward, Barr points first of all to three groups of contrasted N.T. texts[2] in which *kairos* and *chronos* are used in exactly equivalent senses. He comments, with full justification, that 'if there is a difference between *chronos* and *kairos* in New Testament usage, it is clear that it cannot correspond to the distinction between "chronological" and "realistic" time'.[3] Further internal contradictions of the thesis are then examined, particularly as regards the underlying Hebrew usage, and 'as an instrument to guide us in the study of the meaning of words' it is flatly rejected. 'There is no good ground for considering chronological reckoning to be an unessential or secondary element in the biblical understanding of time.'[4] Finally as a result of a careful comparison of the Greek and Hebrew O.T., as well as of an examination of other literature, Barr is prepared to admit that while there are instances in which an opposition between *kairos* and *chronos* may be discerned, there are many examples in which the two words are simply interchangeable.[5] Each usage is to be judged from its context. It may be added that the careful work of Brabant[6] some years earlier fully supports Barr's conclusions.

Since on linguistic grounds Barr's criticism appears to be unanswerable, we have no option but to reject the distinction between *kairos* and *chronos* as a distinction between two conceptions of time; but it by no means follows necessarily that the contrast between 'realistic time' and 'chronological time' has no place in biblical thought. Now it is evident that for the Hebrews certain times, certain moments in their history, possessed special significance. Marsh is absolutely right here. This is the unique contribution of the prophets to our under-

---

[1] *T.W.B.*, 258.
[2] (*a*) Mk. i. 15, Gal. iv. 4; (*b*) Acts iii. 20, iii. 21; (*c*) 1 Pet. i. 5, i. 20, Jude 18. (citing Caird)
[3] *B.W.T.*, 22.   [4] *B.W.T.*, 31.   [5] *B.W.T.*, 41.
[6] F. H. Brabant, *Time and Eternity in Christian Thought*, considers (p. 40) that 'the definition of the words in Hellenistic Greek adequately covers the biblical usage'. This judgement is substantiated by an exhaustive appendix, pp. 235–262.

standing of history in relation to God. The Exodus event was supremely significant in Israelite history; first as a national deliverance; second as the factual basis of the doctrine of God's sovereign control. Hence there is nothing surprising in the fact that constant reference should be made to the Exodus period in the phrase, 'at that time'. But in so far as this phrase is anything more than a linguistic pointer, the weight of interpretation is carried by the 'that', not by the 'time'. Precisely the same remark applies to the use of the same phrase with reference to the Messianic Age. Indeed all such time references are 'realistic' precisely because the meanings of all events of history were understood by the prophets in terms of God. The theological insight that the passage of time brings with it events, opportunities, fulfilment of prophecy, judgement, can stand on its own feet: it can find expression without the need for particular words for time, charged with their own distinctive theological meaning. The insight we owe undoubtedly to the Hebrew prophets: but it can be set down just as clearly in English, where the word 'time' is admittedly neutral.

It is entirely consistent with the prophetic outlook that the time of the Christ-event should be recognized by the New Testament authors as supremely the time of God's revelational and redemptive activity. When Mark writes, 'the time is fulfilled', his use of the definite article simply connects his proclamation to earlier Messianic expectation. This was *the* 'time of fulfilment', ultimately significant for Jew and Gentile alike; but in the phrase, 'time of fulfilment', theological insight is concentrated in the word 'fulfilment'. To announce at the beginning of the Gospel that 'the time is fulfilled' sets the present event in the context of its prophetic foreshadowing. It is *the* time to which the Old Testament has pointed. All this we readily grant—indeed it is vitally important to the unity of the Bible— but it is adequately expressed in the original language by means of a quite ordinary word for time; and it requires no mystique of introducing *kairos*, without translation, into an English sentence in order to express the insight of modern biblical theology. In this sense the realistic view of time can stand legitimately as an important Hebrew insight: the phrase 'realistic time' appears to claim too much however, if it is construed as meaning that the Hebrews had a notably different conception of *time* itself from other peoples. Significance lies not in time but in the events of history.

According to Cullmann the significant thing about the biblical conception of time lies in the relationship between time and eternity. His view is by no means contradictory to the thesis put forward by Marsh, but rather complementary to it. It rests again on a somewhat similar distinction in meaning between two Greek words for time, each of which in the New Testament context is said to take on a peculiarly theological sense not found in the classical use of the language. The point of departure is an alleged difference in mentality, whereby (so it is asserted) the Greeks thought primarily in a spatial metaphor, while the Hebrews were accustomed to think temporally. It is noticeable that Cullmann is more guarded than Marsh, however, in assigning particular meanings to key words. 'To be sure', he writes, 'theological understanding necessarily encounters limits in the separate treatment of a single word'.[1] With this caution he nevertheless draws a distinction between *kairos* and *aiōn*. 'The characteristic thing about *kairos* is that it has to do with a definite *point of time* which has a fixed content, while *aiōn* designates a *duration* of time, a defined or undefined *extent of time*.'[2] Now the New Testament is concerned above all things with redemptive history: and redemptive history lies entirely within God's control. Hence the 'sovereign divine power' alone determines the point in time at which the redemptive process is to take place; and this insight gives to the word *kairos* its specific theological colour.[3] For Cullmann *kairos*, again reproduced in English without translation, becomes the significant point of time deliberately chosen by God for his redemptive act in Christ.

The word *aiōn* serves in the New Testament, we are told, 'to designate both an exactly defined period of time and an undefined and incalculable duration, which we then translate

---

[1] *Christ and Time*, 38.
[2] *loc. cit.*, 39. But N. B. Cullmann's use of 'point' and 'extent', both *spatial* metaphors, in drawing this distinction.
[3] *loc. cit.*, 40.

C

by the word "eternity".'[1] Cullmann insists, however, that 'in this linguistic usage, eternity . . . is not to be interpreted in the Platonic and modern philosophical sense, because from the point of view of time it is seen as time. This is clear, indeed, from the fact that the use of the plural "ages" is particularly preferred when eternity is mentioned.'[2] Eternity is to be thought of not as something different from time but as endless time, incomprehensible to men. 'It means the linking of an unlimited series of limited world periods, whose succession only God is able to survey.'[3] Cullmann insists that we 'must free ourselves completely from all philosophical concepts of time and eternity'[4] if we are to understand the primitive Christian use of *aiōn.*

The primitive Christian conception of time and eternity is therefore to be seen as belonging to a different world from Greek thought. 'On the one side, time does not stand in contrast to God's eternity; on the other side, it is thought of as a straight line, not as a circle. Mention is made of a "beginning" (*archē*) and an "end" (*telos*)'.[5] God's lordship over time is rightly asserted; and what purports to be a peculiarly Christian picture of time and eternity is developed, being represented diagrammatically by a continuous straight-line. The Christ-event is seen as the 'mid-point' of the time-line: a point of central significance rather than of exact division. Along with the division of linear time by the Christ-event goes the corresponding distinction between 'this present age', up to the time of the eschatological event, and the 'age to come', thereafter. In contrast with Judaism, primitive Christianity treats the mid-point of the time-line as present reality. 'The chronologically new thing which Christ brought for the faith of Primitive Christianity consists in the fact that *for the believing Christian the mid-point, since Easter, no longer lies in the future*',[6] as of course it does for Judaism. In the subsequent treatment the analogy with D-day and V-day in the second world war is fruitfully exploited. In Christ the essential decisive victory over evil is already won. The age of the Church is the period in which the warfare is to be carried to a victorious conclusion: final victory is assured by the victory of Christ, and the 'when'

---

[1] *loc. cit.*, 45.   [2] *loc. cit.*, 45f.   [3] *loc. cit.*, 46.   [4] *loc. cit.*, 48.
[5] *loc. cit.*, 51.   [6] *loc. cit.*, 81: illustrative diagram, 83.

of that consummation is therefore a matter of irrelevance for primitive Christianity. In the age of the Church the fact that 'sin is still present, although the Holy Spirit is already at work, is definite proof that it is a "redemptive necessity" for time itself to continue in order to carry the redemptive history to its goal'.[1] Thus the whole process of God's activity, from before the creation till after the *parousia*, is to be thought of according to Cullmann as a process in 'linear time'. To make any philosophical distinction between time and eternity is to misunderstand completely the biblical insight into the things of God.

In examining the linguistic basis of Cullmann's work, Barr comments that this thesis 'is on the whole rather less erroneous than the former, for it is at least true that *aiōn* never means a point of time, even if it is not true that *kairos* never means a period or extent of time.'[2] After pointing to actual examples of the use of both words, however, he admits that 'when an "age" in the sense of one of the great epochs of the world's duration is meant, it is much more *common* to use *aiōn* than to use *kairos*'.[3] Putting his finger on several inconsistencies in Cullmann's linguistic treatment of the alleged distinction between these two words, Barr criticizes strongly the use of such phrases as 'the *kairos* concept', both on the ground of ambiguity (since it disguises the polysemy of *kairos*) and because transliteration without translation merely bluffs the reader into accepting an apparently technical term. Cullmann's 'presentation of the series of kairoi is often far remote from actual usage of *kairos* in the New Testament'.[4]

Turning to the treatment of *aiōn*, Barr disposes of the 'argument—that the use of the plural for "eternity" proves that continuance, and not cessation, of time is intended', as a *non-sequitur* which tacitly ignores the well-known fact that a plural form does not necessarily mean 'a plurality and variety of the objects designated by the singular.'[5] The implication in Cullmann's work that linear time is to be extended indefinitely, backward and forward, is shown to be based on the error of giving *aiōn* its free sense when it occurs in a bound phrase, such as *eis ton aiōna*. The bound phrases demand translation as 'from eternity', 'for ever', 'in perpetuity', and the like. Neither

[1] *loc. cit.*, 93.   [2] *B.W.T.*, 47.   [3] *B.W.T.*, 48.
[4] *B.W.T.*, 63.   [5] *B.W.T.*, 64.

here nor in the corresponding Hebrew usage do they tell us anything about the conception of time itself. 'Cullmann's— scheme is in fact a homogeneous representation of his own view of time'.[1] It cannot be derived from the lexical stock of the New Testament except by extremely unnatural treatment of linguistic usage.

Once again it must be admitted that Barr's criticisms are exceedingly damaging. The position is easily misunderstood however, if we allow ourselves to forget that the critic is a linguistic specialist, while the one criticized has the broader theological interests. And it is therefore gratifying to find that Barr himself is at pains to add: 'I am by no means trying to prove that Cullmann is wrong in his contention that there is no qualitative distinction between what we call "time" and what we call "eternity": I am showing only that this contention cannot be proved by Cullmann's study of the vocabulary.'[2] A further observation, which sums up his linguistic objections succinctly, is applicable equally to Cullmann and to Marsh: 'The basic fault in the whole procedure is the assumption that the vocabulary stock is laid out in a pattern which correlates exactly with the mental pattern of New Testament thinking about time.'[2] For this reason Cullmann's rejoinder, published as an addendum to the third edition of *Christ and Time*, is important not only for its implicit acceptance of the linguistic criticism, but also as expressing the view that 'linear time' as a background 'can be derived from the New Testament conception of eschatology quite independently from the lexicographical method which Barr rejects'. 'Linear time', Cullmann contends, 'is merely a framework, which as such never was an object of serious reflexion on the part of the early Christians.'[3] The disclaimers of the two protagonists at least put this highly technical discussion in its proper perspective, and for this we may be thankful.

BARR'S POSITIVE CONTRIBUTION

A story currently circulating in the oral tradition of the sciences illustrates rather nicely the inadequacy of a too mechanical approach to the problems of translation. An

[1] *B.W.T.*, 74.   [2] *B.W.T.*, 80.   [3] *Christ and Time*, 3rd ed., *xxxi*.

electronic brain was given the job of translating into Chinese the proverb, 'Out of sight, out of mind'. Subsequently a second electronic brain, rendering the result back into English, produced the translation, 'Invisible lunatic'! Exact verbal equivalents in different languages are discoverable only where there is a true meeting of minds.

An essential preliminary to the study of distinctions between different words within a given language is the realization that the vocabulary is to a large extent inherited. These are the noises we make when we wish to communicate. We have not invented them: we have learned them. Those who write in any language, ancient or modern, have to make shift with the words available; words do not normally correlate at all exactly with such philosophical distinctions as we may wish to make. Even technical terms must be derived from previously existing language, and such terms never form more than a small fraction of the vocabulary used in a technical communication. The English word 'time' is required to do service in both technical and non-technical senses, sometimes with the meaning 'occasion', sometimes with the meaning 'period', as well as serving for 'clock-time' and in more abstract senses. The meaning intended can usually be tested by word-substitution. Moreover, two languages will normally have different ranges of words available; which means that translation can never proceed according to some invariable scheme of equivalents. The overlapping or non-overlapping of the lexical stocks of two given languages provides therefore no adequate basis for contrasting the philosophical concepts of two peoples.

Words must not be taken out of their syntactic relation to complete items of communication, such as the clause or the sentence.[1] Translation, if it is to have any validity, must render an actual communication in one language into an actual communication in another. The 'concept method' leads only to bogus translation. Generally speaking, etymological considerations must not be used to bring out the so-called 'inner meaning' of a word: the price is mistranslation. Responsible translation 'involves the leaving aside of etymological information, and

---

[1] 'Phrases . . . like words themselves, are elements in the larger type of linguistic structure such as the sentence, and it is in sentences that the real theological thinking is done.' *The Semantics of Biblical Language*, 234.

of senses which the words have elsewhere than in the communications being handled'.[1] Accurate translation will always serve as a valuable corrective to false interpretations of particular words.

Barr then considers in close detail the actual translation of biblical Hebrew into Greek, Latin, Syriac, and Coptic, with special reference to the vocabulary of time; concluding that in spite of the fact that different languages have quite different lexical stocks, a knowledge of usage is a sufficient guide to an adequate translation. It would be 'hard to maintain that large and essential areas of the message communicated by the New Testament were quite lost in languages other than Greek because such languages did not reproduce the shape of the Greek lexical distribution'.[2] In fact, 'theological meaning belongs to the *utterances*, in which elements of the lexical stock are syntactically combined with others'.[3] This dictum, which one might have supposed would be self-evident, but for the fog in which the whole subject has become enveloped, must be accepted as a beacon to guide our discussion.

Now when we resolve to extract biblical conceptions and meanings only from explicit utterances, it becomes apparent that the delineation of a biblical concept of time, and of time in relation to eternity, is a very circumscribed proceeding. Barr remarks on 'the very serious shortage within the Bible of the kind of *actual statement* about "time" or "eternity" which could form a sufficient basis for a Christian philosophical-theological view of time'.[4] Hence the welter of opposing views of the problem offered by a number of biblical theologians.[5] As regards the limited question whether in the biblical view time has a beginning, Barr is prepared to hazard the opinion that 'the importance of the creation stories' may possibly suggest that 'time began with the creation of the world', and that 'there is at least some case for talking about "eternity" as a reality other than time'.[6] Aside from this there exists very little material on which to work apart from Ecclesiastes: a book which might be held to support a cyclic view of time in some sense, but which is strongly suspect among biblical theologians (perhaps without justification) as being under the influence of Greek thought.

[1] *B.W.T.*, 115.   [2] *B.W.T.*, 127.   [3] *B.W.T.*, 128.
[4] *B.W.T.*, 131 f.   [5] *B.W.T.*, 143 f.   [6] *B.W.T.*, 145.

Hence Barr is driven to assert that 'if such a thing as a Christian doctrine of time has to be developed, the work of discussing and developing it must belong not to biblical but to philosophical theology;'[1] a view which I for one can readily accept. It is undeniable that the Hebrews thought of *history* as a process controlled by God, and guided towards a goal. Undoubtedly this view of history was taken over by the New Testament writers. And perhaps we have no right to ask for more: for history is concerned with the acts of God, particularly the mighty acts by which Christian salvation is given; while time is no more than a framework within which history moves. The early Christians had experiential knowledge of salvation but they were entirely innocent of any kind of sophistication.

Whatever view of time the biblical authors held was clearly not a formulated view. They had neither the interest nor the analytical skill to examine the question; and it is not for us to foist upon them either a naive or a sophisticated theory of our own devising. Marsh strikes the right note when he says:

'We have no wish to argue that the Greeks were philosophers, the Hebrews not, and that because the Hebrews wrote the Bible (in Hebrew and Greek) their views are right and relevant and all Greek philosophy a vain study for the Christian. Rather would we claim that we may dispense neither with the profound religious insight of the Hebrews nor with the careful philosophizing of the Greeks. Christian thought about time, eternity and history must spring from the insights that the Bible possesses and imparts; their systematization is the enviable if difficult task of the Christian philosopher as heir to the Greek.'[2]

We must make up our minds however, how far the views formulated by Marsh and Cullmann are acceptable as tentative insights into the earliest Christian thought about the redemption-history. In so far as linear time signifies the common-sense view that event follows event in a steady unidirectional movement, it is probably reasonable to suppose that the earliest Christians thought in terms of linear time. In so far as they thought of the Christ-event as central in *history*,

---

[1] *B.W.T.*, 149.   [2] J. Marsh, *The Fulness of Time*, 16.

if not in time, we can hardly disagree. We tacitly accept this in our dating, as Cullmann points out. We can agree too that the decisive events of the redemption-history are fixed by God: and that their times are significant on account of their content. Further than this we cannot go. And we may well incline to the view that any adequate understanding of the time of the eschatological event was beyond the intellectual capacity of the New Testament authors—as it may well be beyond our own. Yet manifestly, as heirs to a long philosophical and theological tradition, not to mention newer scientific insights, we should naturally expect to approach the question in terms quite different from those employed in the New Testament. What the New Testament authors express somewhat naively must be re-expressed in the light of all further development of human thought; providing only that this is accomplished without distortion of the essential revelation which the biblical utterances contain.

III

TIME AND CHANGE

IF we are to make any progress in the understanding of time and eternity, and the relation between them in theological thinking, we must look first outside the biblical revelation. Philosophy can help us to avoid the numerous pitfalls of a general investigation, but cannot solve the basic question, What is time? Indeed, its failure suggests that this fundamental enquiry is of too exacting a nature for the human mind. A new approach may therefore be justified. Instead of trying to solve an apparently intractable conundrum, let us restrict ourselves to the question, *How can we usefully think about time?* A word of warning, though. This is not the solely practical question which horologists have to face professionally. It is not the design of clocks that we are concerned with; nor yet the principles of exact time-measurement, except incidentally. But rather, Can we form a conception of what we talk about when we use the word 'time'? A conception, moreover, which is not so naive as to suppose that there is no problem outstanding. A conception which takes account of the facts of experience, both general and technical; which allows us to give meaning to the indications of our clocks; and which is not an affront to the philosophical intelligence.

This is our immediate programme. A corresponding enquiry with regard to eternity must come later. And then, equipped with two concepts of agreed usefulness in their respective spheres, we can hope to say something about the relation of time and eternity in theological thinking.

THE SENSE OF TIME

In the first chapter I referred to the suggestion that we all have a basic sense of time, more fundamental than clock-time and the solar day. 'Biological time' and 'psychological time' were mentioned as possibilities, both different in some way from solar time. Though we were unable then to indicate in what sense we could legitimately use the word 'different', yet the existence of a basic sense of time is a clue worth following.

So far as human beings are concerned there are certain obvious large-scale rhythms with which we are all familiar. Some occupy times of the order of a few hours: waking and sleeping, tummy full and tummy empty. The obvious connection of our personal habits with the hours of light and darkness would prevent us from placing undue significance on the former. The latter reminds us however that there is 'something within' which tells us when it is time for the next meal, more or less: a metabolic process which 'judges' the passage of 'time' rather roughly. Rhythms of a different character divide our life-span into discrete periods: childhood, puberty, adolescence, manhood, senescence. And though the stages are by no means sharply marked, and it is equally legitimate to regard the stages of life as forming a relatively smooth progression, yet the changes of which we speak constitute a uni-directional movement in time, at a rate which is substantially the same for different individuals. Again there are well-known rhythms of a more rapid character: breathing and the heart-beat. While all these are temporal phenomena, marking the passage of time in some sense, none has quite that constancy to qualify as a basis for our innate sense of time. Yet experiments are on record of human subjects, shut up in darkened sound-proof rooms for periods of up to four days, who were able to estimate the passage of time to an accuracy of 1 per cent.[1] Clearly the innate sense of time is real.

What is its cause? How does it work? We do not know. One clue may come from the study of the very weak but quite detectable electric rhythms of the brain. The electroencephalogram enables us to measure the difference in electrical potential between two metal plates in contact with the outside of the skull. The variations in potential comprise a number of rhythms of different periods. Some appear to be associated with mental activity, others with resting. One, the so-called alpha-rhythm, of frequency about ten per second, is so persistent that

[1] R. B. MacLeod and M. T. Roff, *Acta Psychol.*, X, 389–423.

it has been acclaimed by some investigators as the basic clock.[1] Such a judgement, however, is probably premature. Nor is the sense of time restricted to the human species. A vast amount of evidence has accumulated to show that all forms of life have some sort of awareness of the passage of time: sometimes highly developed, sometimes capable of being deceived by a clever experiment. It is now well established that the honey bee is able to return to the hive from remarkable distances, taking its bearings from the sun and making use of some sort of time-keeping mechanism in order to compensate for the sun's apparent movement. Migrant birds apparently navigate in much the same way. At a lower level, diurnal rhythms of habit or colour-change are observed in anemones and crabs; and these can be maintained in the absence of those external stimuli which might be supposed to control them. An effect known as photo-periodism is observed even in plants. A group of American scientists[2] has studied a number of these effects in various creatures in a laboratory at the South Pole, where it is possible to compensate exactly for the apparent movement of the sun by a counter-rotation of their enclosure; and it seems to be established that time-regulation is not controlled by external stimuli of any kind.

It is a far cry from men to birds, crabs, anemones, and even plants. There is nothing here to feed our ego. Whatever innate sense of time we can claim to possess is shared in some way, and often very precisely, by the entire organic kingdom. Though we should not be justified in supposing that the actual mechanism is everywhere the same, we may at least ask what there is in common throughout the whole range of living things. There is the individual cell; a variable but in some ways a constant building unit. When we remember that the outer membrane of a cell is an electrically-charged surface; that impulses are carried through the nervous system by a succession of minute electrical discharges; that the central nervous system consists of a vast number of inter-connected cells[3]; and that the electrical alpha-rhythm has been identified as a possible clue: we have at least a hint as to how such a remarkable phenome-

---

[1] See G. J. Whitrow, *The Natural Philosophy of Time*, 69–71, for a summary.
[2] K. C. Hamner, *et. al.*, *Nature*, **195**, 476–80 (1962).
[3] About ten-thousand-million in the human brain.

non as biological time-keeping is universal in the organic world.

Without a knowledge of the mechanism of the biological clock we can hardly expect to know much about its origin. That it is in some way a product of evolution goes almost without saying; and that those clearly marked periodicities which keep time with the solar day, tidal movements, and the like, are connected with the external conditions under which evolution took place can be treated as reasonably certain also. Once formed, such temporal rhythms are presumably inherited, and prove to be resistant to further change. What is no more than a pattern of temporal behaviour at the lower levels of life may provide the mechanism which underlies what we know as a sense of time. The sense of time, however, as a fact of consciousness is qualitatively distinct from the biological system, or mechanism, which is its material basis. This distinction is highly significant. While further scientific research may be expected to show the mechanism of the biological clock, it can hardly tell us more about the innate sense of time than we know already. A barrier of a qualitative character marks off the area amenable to scientific investigation from that which is strictly interior to the experiencing subject.

The rhythms are objective: the sense of time subjective. The one may be investigated in other subjects, and even by other people in me. I may know as a fact of science that I am like other organisms in the possession of a biological clock, which objectively controls various metabolic processes, and which 'ticks' on into senescence until it stops altogether. But I know also what it *feels like* to have such a clock, and this is what I mean when I say that I have an innate sense of time. The sense of time is the subjective aspect of what is objectively a biological clock. Does this imply that the sense of time is therefore illusory? Not at all. Reality must be accorded both to the objective and the subjective.[1] In somewhat the same way, a wound is real (objective), but so is the pain (subjective): the

---

[1] The word 'objective' means, 'pertaining to an object external to the person who perceives it'. The word 'subjective' means, 'pertaining to the experiencing or perceiving subject'. It is not true that 'objective' is a reputable word, and 'subjective' a disreputable word. To cast doubts on something by referring to it as 'purely subjective' is on all fours with the scorn that classes intellectual problems as of 'purely academic interest'. In either case the 'sniff' is without justification.

chemical composition of food is real, but so is the taste. Are we then to dismiss the sense of time as something secondary or as a mere epiphenomenon? No. It is true that secondary qualities, unlike primary, are not amenable to scientific investigation; and that we commonly restrict the word 'phenomenon' to that which is open to public inspection. But so far as I myself am concerned, experience is a unity; and I know my own sense of time with the same certainty as I know the existence of your biological clock. If we are wise, we shall accept the validity of all knowledge, and recognize that all knowledge is personal knowledge. I am saying no more than that some of my knowledge can be shared, while some cannot. The sense of time is subjective in precisely this sense: we cannot share it, but it is none the less real.[1]

An interesting epistemological digression would be to examine how it comes about that we can recognize that each of us has experience of this character, admitting that it is impossible to share it. Such an investigation would draw presumably on the fact of our common cultural heritage, and on the processes of learning in infancy and adolescence. We should perhaps have to admit that apart from these influences our sense of time might not have developed quite in the way it has developed. Child psychologists inform us that the sense of past and future comes only in stages as we grow up. Conceivably the same is true as regards the evolutionary history of the race. Yet though we recognize that cultural influences are profound, there must be something in each of us which cultural influences merely call into action, some latent possibility awaiting development. So too with the race. Something of the same kind is involved in the recognition and naming of colours, for instance. We can agree that red is red, and that green is green, even though we cannot actually share the subjective experience of seeing either. Cultural influence and the capacity to distinguish colours together provide the clue to the fact that we can converse intelligibly about colour. Cultural influence and the capacity to distinguish times together account fully for our being able to converse intelligibly about temporal matters. The only essential difference, as I see it, between the sense of colour and the sense of time, is that one

[1] M. Polanyi, *Personal Knowledge, Towards a Post-critical Philosophy*, 373 f.

is my subjective response to what is outside my skin, while the other is my subjective response to what is inside it.

To return to the main line of the argument. The sense of time is the subjective experience of consciousness corresponding to the possession of a biological clock. The next step is to recognize *what* it is about the rhythm of the biological clock which we interpret or experience as a sense of time. This is a step which, I believe, cannot be made strictly logically. It is essentially an intuitive step; but one which subsequent discussion will be seen to justify. Perhaps the word 'rhythm' is inappropriate, and to a degree misleading: it seems hardly likely that we unconsciously 'count the ticks'. What was a half-playful description of a mechanical clock is no help here. What I want to suggest is that the existence of what we have called a rhythm is no more than the marking into segments of a continuing biological change. Something inside the organism which is me, which in principle is open to inspection, is constantly changing. That objective *change*, of whatever kind it may be (material, electrical, chemical), is experienced subjectively as a sense of time. In suggesting that there is continuing change, I do not imply a constant rate of change: that would be to invoke time, indeed public clock time, prematurely; and would be totally unjustifiable. Simply change: change continuing without intermission from cradle to grave. As long as change continues, we have the sense of time. The sense of time is the subjective experience of consciousness corresponding to the continuing change in that something (whatever it is) which we recognize objectively as a biological clock. Indeed, we might say that *each of us is a biological clock* : a fully conscious one. We cannot prove that this is so. Nor can we prove the contrary. This is an intuitive step in the argument, which will be justified by its usefulness as a principle of interpretation.

Of course there is a sense in which we do not seem to have advanced beyond Aristotle's conception of time. But there is an all-important difference. Aristotle defined time as that which can be numbered, or counted, in the movement from the earlier to the later. True, he recognized movement as the key to the question: and by movement he meant what we mean by change. But, we must ask, movement or change of what? For Aristotle that which changes is external to him: the sun, the stars, the flow of water; in principle the hands of a mechanical clock, if the anachronism is permissible. For us the essential article, the biological clock, is internal and therefore not open to inspection by the person who experiences the sense of time. So the case is entirely different. My sense of time is my subjective experience of having (or being) an organism which is in a continuing state of change; whereas for Aristotle time is the interpretation of a state of change external to the percipient. We agree that continuing change is the essential clue. And as we shall see, change is that which is common to every time-measuring device; be it biological clock, sundial, or pendulum. But the distinction between a change proceeding within my own organism and a change proceeding outside my skin is absolute. The one gives me the subjective experience which I call a sense of time. The other permits me to design an instrument which is serviceable for indicating what I already know as time in my conscious experience.

From this point onwards I shall treat the sense of time as a primordial fact of personal knowledge, the subjective experience of that continuing change which proceeds unceasingly in my biological organism.

SCALES OF TIME

In principle, any changing phenomenon in the external world can be pressed into service as a relatively independent device for assessing time. Even one's own pulse is effectively such a phenomenon, already marked for counting, since it is observable with the fingers as externally objective in exactly the same way as another man's pulse: and it is on record that Galileo so employed it for timing the swing of the sanctuary lamps when he should have been otherwise occupied. Yet the fact that the pulse gives a series of discrete beats places it too obviously in the clock class for it to be an ideal illustration of general principles. The flow of water through a hole so that the level falls in a tank, and the angular movement of shadows cast by the sun on the ground, are simpler phenomena which provide a steady and continuous indication of change, And this is quite sufficient for our purpose.

Let us then imagine the situation at the dawn of history. We have an innate sense of time, but no clocks or sundials. We know simply that various external objects are in a state of change: they present a different configuration later than earlier, as that distinction is given to us primordially in consciousness. We hit on the idea of using one or more of these continuously changing phenomena, in order to provide an agreed public standard of how-much-later, i.e. a standard of time. We set up two 'clocks', in one of which we observe the fall of water in a tank as it runs out through a small hole, and in the other the angular movement of the shadow of a vertical rod cast by the sun. At sunrise we mark the level of the water and the line of the shadow. When the water has fallen one foot, we again mark the level and the shadow, continuing in this manner throughout the day. In this way we construct two possible time-scales. Both are entirely arbitrary, yet both mark the passage of time. How do they compare? The divisions of the water clock are equally spaced, having been made so: the divisions of the sun clock get progressively longer as we proceed along the scale. Both are more or less reproducible, provided we start first thing in the morning: but if we start again at mid-day with the tank filled to the original level, an entirely different set of markings would have to be made on the sun clock. The two scales follow different laws of time: not sur-prisingly, since they depend on unconnected phenomena. (Any number of such scales could be devised, all equally arbitrary; and in general they would not be in agreement.)

Now anyone with a knowledge of physical science will readily understand why these two scales differ.[1] But at this stage of the argument we must put all this later knowledge out of our minds. Both scales are arbitrary. The question is not, Which clock gives us the correct scale of time? but, Which clock gives us the more useful scale? In practice of course it is easier for everybody to observe the sun's shadow than it would be to equip everybody with identical water tanks. But the question of usefulness is not decided simply on this ground. Though as a matter of historical fact mankind has accepted

[1] In terms of solar time the square of the velocity of flow from the tank is proportional to the depth of water remaining. Consequently if the water clock is given a scale of equal divisions, the divisions of the sun clock become progressively longer, as the water level falls, and the flow is slower—slower, that is, as measured by solar time, which *we* accept as standard.

the sun clock as standard from time immemorial, the real criterion of its usefulness becomes apparent only as scientific knowledge advances. Prior to that, the choice of the sun for time-keeping is rather in the nature of a shrewd guess; prompted no doubt by the fact that the larger units of solar time, day and night, are already given. None of this, however, should blind us to the fact that the choice of a solar time-scale is both arbitrary in the first instance, and fortuitously convenient in the long run.

What is the criterion of usefulness by which the solar time-scale came to be accepted as a universal standard? Broadly two groups of facts, both connected with the science of mechanics, and together constituting a criterion of internal consistency.

First of all we glance at Newton's classic but misleading definition of absolute time: that which of itself flows equably without relation to anything external. We know now that there is no such thing as absolute time, any more than there is such a thing as absolute space. Einstein's Theory of Relativity, accepted both on grounds of theoretical elegance and its ability to explain certain small discrepancies in classical mechanics, has finally ousted the conceptions of absolute space and time. Although Newton predicated an absolute, true, and mathematical time, in terms of which to express the equations of motion of classical mechanics, the scale which he used implicitly was none other than that provided by the apparent movement of the sun, suitably averaged over the year. The mathematical elegance of his theory of planetary motion, and its ability to account correctly for the observational laws known since the time of Kepler, were simply a measure of the usefulness of the mechanical concepts with which he worked, including of course the time-scale which was already conventional. To recognize this fact is not in any sense to disparage Newton's epoch-making work. Indeed it is to see exactly where his achievement lay. He introduced consistency into the theoretical characterization of a vast range of phenomena. And the fact that he was able to do so, though this significance escaped him, established solar time as a conception of the utmost usefulness in bringing scientific order into a realm of apparent chaos. That solar time should be identified with absolute, true, and mathematical time was a passing error in the growth of science.

The other group of facts which underpins the usefulness of

D

solar time is provided by the study of harmonic oscillations. In the earlier stages of scientific advance such oscillations could all be comprised within the realm of the purely mechanical: the motion of the pendulum, the oscillation of a helical spring, the sounding of a musical instrument, the vibration of the air during the passage of a sound wave. Of course, man's own innate sense of time had already led him to recognize the motions of the pendulum and the spring as approximately isochronous. When, however, classical mechanics proved capable of reducing all these motions to a single harmonic pattern, whose characteristic equation contained implicitly the isochronous behaviour, this extension of the realm of consistent representation even further established the usefulness of the underlying conception of time. Further extension of the theory of harmonic oscillation to embrace electrical phenomena underlines the usefulness of this Newtonian conception of time throughout almost the whole range of physical science.

But of course it is to be remembered that the sense of time is our subjective experience of change in what is objectively a biological process. Time itself cannot be further identified than in terms of our own subjective consciousness, or personal knowledge. The manufacture of clocks is simply the harnessing of some external continuing change to be an indication of what we already experience as time. All such indicators, and their corresponding scales, are essentially arbitrary. The adoption of any one of them as public time, or for scientific purposes, depends only on the criterion of usefulness. Solar time has proved itself by this criterion; apart, that is, from certain discrepancies which are negligible under normal conditions. This means in practice that solar time provides a quantitative temporal framework, ensuring the internal consistency of the mathematical structure of the physical sciences. Nevertheless, the argument is in some degree circular, for the rotation of the earth on its axis is itself an item of the physical universe. This circularity need not distress us however, if our criterion is usefulness. Indeed it is unavoidable. The innate sense of time, which remains the basis of all temporal conceptions, cannot be made truly quantitative and therefore publicly available, except by reference to objective change in the world around us. That so much can be reduced to order, and consistently exhibited in equations involving a time variable derived from one item of the physical universe, is an indication of unity and rationality in the created order which has obvious implications for philosophical theology.

One result of the adoption of solar time as standard is that those other temporal changes in the external world, which in principle might have been chosen as a basis for public time, are now expressible in terms of laws involving solar time as a variable. And the human biological clock itself, though it provides the temporal sense as a fact of consciousness, comes to be thought of as a mechanism whose time-keeping may be judged by the external standard of solar time. Looked at in this way, the biological clock is distinctly unreliable over long periods. Older people are familiar with the experience that time seems to pass more rapidly than when they were young. In general our bodily processes become slower with advancing age, and it may be presumed that this applies to the biological clock also—slower, that is, as judged by public time. Hence our sense that public time flows more rapidly as we advance in years. Such an effect, of course, does not prevent us from estimating the passage of public time with some degree of accuracy at any given point in life. The change in what we might call our implicit 'conversion factor' is quite slow; and we make the necessary mental adjustment without specific effort. Nevertheless it is a strange commentary upon us that, having an innate sense of time, which is the basis of our entire temporal reckoning, we pass the responsibility for time-keeping to the sun and the public clock. In this sense we are truly the slaves of time.

ACCURATE TIME-KEEPING

The theory and practice of exact time-keeping are fascinating subjects in their own right. We are concerned with them here only in so far as they affect our conception of public or clock time. In mentioning a few points of general interest, I shall endeavour simply to bring out certain principles implicit in our modern understanding of the world process as a process in time.

So far we have tacitly ignored the fact that the solar day varies in length throughout the course of the year. How can we justify such a statement if solar time is our standard? Three converging lines of argument are our justification, and the implications are interesting. In the first place, if a good-quality pendulum clock is compared with the daily transit of the sun, the variation of the interval from mid-day to mid-day is exhibited directly in terms of the time-scale of the clock. Hence either the clock or the solar day is variable. Secondly, bearing in mind that the earth's orbit around the sun is elliptical and that the axis of rotation of the earth is inclined, a theoretical explanation of the observed variation can be offered in quantitative terms: whereas it is not possible to offer any convincing explanation of a corresponding periodic error in the clock. In the third place, relative to the apparent motions of the stars, the clock keeps relatively good time. Although public time is ostensibly based upon the sun's apparent movement, consistency demands that we place reliance on a properly constructed clock rather than on the time indicated by the sun on any particular day. The mechanical clock therefore replaces the sun-dial, and is adjusted to read *mean* solar time. If this argument appears somewhat irrelevant in the present context, it illustrates nevertheless an essential stage of sophistication. It is the first and most elementary instance of a quite general principle: whereby internal consistency in time-keeping requires that we place greater and greater reliance upon the most perfect mechanism that can be devised, rather than on the obvious and rudimentary. In effect, we are merely repeating the kind of step which was taken in remote antiquity, when the indications of the sun were preferred to man's own innate sense of time, even though the latter is the logical basis of all time-keeping.

With the development of technique, the so-called quartz clock came to replace mechanical clocks where the greatest precision is required. This clock depends on the principle that an accurately cut crystal of quartz can be maintained in longitudinal vibration by means of a suitable electric circuit; whose frequency of oscillation is held constant to an exceedingly high degree, provided the temperature of the crystal is carefully controlled. Precision in time-keeping has been extended by this technique to the astonishing accuracy of one part in ten-thousand-million, representing an error of only one second in about three hundred years. The electric tick at high frequency therefore replaces the mechanical tick of the pendulum clock in the standard of time maintained by the National Physical Laboratory and the corresponding institutions in other advanced countries. Until the year 1964, the unit of time was still defined in terms of the mean solar day: though the precision of the quartz clock enables us to detect a slow decrease in the rate of revolution of the earth on its axis, i.e. a secular change in the length of the mean solar day. Here is another instance of the principle referred to already: that in the interest of internal consistency reliance tends to shift from the sun to the most perfect time-keeping device which can be constructed.

The latest technique, still under development, employs a device known as the Laser, a light source emitting a monochromatic beam of quite exceptional purity and coherence. The frequency associated with the light wave is of course several orders of magnitude higher than the frequency of a quartz clock, and is known from independent measurements of (a) the velocity of light, (b) the number of light waves in the standard metre length. Since clock-time enters into the determination of the velocity of light, the frequency is expressed in terms of clock-time. Over relatively short periods this new technique leads to even higher precision in time-keeping; and from 1964 onwards the laser will provide the standard time for the most precise scientific purposes. Another example of the same principle.

At this point the layman may well ask where all this is leading. What is it in aid of? Nobody needs to know the time to this accuracy for ordinary purposes. There are technical and scientific applications where such precision is essential; but that is not the point of mentioning the latest developments here. What then is its significance?

The Theory of Relativity (discussed briefly in Chapter VIII), which is now firmly established as the most general and consistent formulation of the laws of nature, requires that we conceive physical reality, not in terms of two independent frameworks, space and time, but in terms of a single continuum, space-time. Its fundamental postulate is the absolute constancy of the velocity of light, relative to all observers, no matter how they move in relation to one another. The frequencies associated with various monochromatic light waves are also thought to be absolute constants of nature, characteristic of the atoms which emit them. Hence it is clear that our *units* both of length and time can be defined absolutely in terms of the velocity of light and the light waves from atoms of a particular element. The metre is defined no longer as the length between two marks on a standard metal bar, but as the length containing so many waves of the chosen monochromatic radiation. And the second is defined no longer as a fraction of the mean solar day, but as the time interval containing so many oscillations of the chosen radiation. We then possess a unified system of measures which depends ultimately on the constancy of nature, rather than on a piece of apparatus made by man. Here is one more shift away from the obvious and rudimentary to the more highly sophisticated: and it looks like the final step.

What is distinctly worth noticing, however, is that the shift towards higher sophistication is more than a mere change of instruments: it involves new concepts. The plain man thinks of length in terms of the space between two marks on a bar. He thinks of time in terms of the interval between two ticks of a clock. For scientific purposes both concepts have been refined to the point when they must be replaced by definitions in terms of the constant behaviour of the atom chosen as standard. Nature itself is providing the 'absolute' units of measurement. And this change of concept, made possible by improvements in technique, becomes necessary in the interest of logical consistency.

We have come a long way from the innate sense of time and the simple sundial. If we are still not clear what time *is*, at least the basic principles of time measurement have been laid bare. We have begun to see how we can usefully think about time. We have seen the importance of internal consistency as the criterion for judging a scale of time. We have moved from the entirely arbitrary to the possibly absolute unit of measurement. Yet in spite of all sophistication we do well to emphasise afresh that objective biological change, experienced subjectively in consciousness, is the basis of all time-keeping. This insight, I believe, is the scientific counterpart of Heidegger's shrewd observation that 'Temporality is the reason for the clock', and 'in a certain manner Dasein itself is the clock'.[1] In order to have an agreed standard of time for public and scientific purposes, we make use of objective change of various kinds

---

[1] *Being and Time*, 466 and 469.

outside ourselves: first the sun, then the best pendulum clocks, then the quartz crystal, finally the atom itself. Progress has been from the obvious and rudimentary to the more and more highly sophisticated. None of this must blind us however to the simplest fact of our experience. *Time itself is not a fact of the external world*, as Aristotle realised. *Change is a fact of nature*. And biological change within our own organism is experienced subjectively in consciousness as time.[1] Time, in so far as we dare to give it a specification, is a fact of personal knowledge, integral to our understanding of ourselves and our surroundings; for we are subject to change and experience it subjectively. That is our essentially human condition.

[1] The reader may raise the objection that time is more fundamental than change: how can there be change except in time? Are we not putting the scientific cart before the philosophical horse? Since the step I have taken is central to the argument of this and the succeeding chapter, it must not be glossed over. I presume that the innate sense of time is not in dispute though its interpretation may be: and as a general proposition I readily concede the primacy of mind over matter. The human mind, however, is not to be thought of as detached from, or independent of, its material embodiment. The familiar dichotomy of mind and body is not a division or separation of parts but a distinction of function. A human person is a whole in which the mental and material functions are interdependent, and I must think of myself as a psycho-somatic unity. No doubt pure minds exist; but in the human species (and perhaps to a lesser extent in lower forms of life) mind is associated with a high degree of organization and complexity of matter. This being so, we must not interpret the deliveries of mind in a manner which divorces it entirely from the functioning of the material organism in which it is embodied.

True, the sense of time includes (and indeed involves logically) the distinction between before and after. The distinction between before and after may be correlated with (a) external change, (b) internal biological change, and (c) change in the content of the mind, either as it considers the external world or develops its own thoughts: and in this statement correlation is to be understood in a neutral sense, which does not yet presuppose the primordial character of any one kind of change at the expense of the other two. Recognizing the correlation, however, we must try to decide which kind of change is primary for a human person. I would hold that (a) is not primary, since the sense of time persists even under circumstances where no external change is perceptible; and that (c) is not primary, since we are conscious that time *has passed* even when the mind has been completely inactive. Internal biological change remains as the only change which persists throughout life, independently of both external environment and the conscious activity of the mind. For this reason it must be held to be primary.

How can there be change except in time? In one sense there cannot. The 'time' in terms of which changes of type (a) and (c) are known is apprehended as an immediate fact of personal knowledge by a person who is a psycho-somatic unity. 'After' is distinguished from 'before' because the distinguishing subject is not in precisely the same state. Internal biological change is what constitutes the experiencing subject a 'clock'. Such intimate change is not known by the experiencing subject *as change*, but subjectively as time, because he locates all external change of type (a) and all conscious mental change of type (b) in terms of it.

―――――

IV

TIME'S ARROW

ONE of the more fascinating exercises of the imagination is to suppose time to run backwards. The result is a topsy-turvy 'looking-glass' world in which the queerest things happen. Broken china on the floor pieces itself together and rises to the shelf. The chicken goes into the shell, which closes around it. Thunder precedes the lightning. Such fantasy can be simulated by running a cinematograph film backwards; and the sound-track, also reversed, provides a suitably grotesque commentary.

Our mental experiments in time-reversal tend to dwell on the situations which we recognize as queer, i.e. as physically impossible; but time-reversal as such does not result necessarily in the impossible. Two cases should be distinguished: (1) A series of events in time, between which no direct connections exist, can be imagined as reversed without a ridiculous situation arising. I sit down at the piano and in turn strike the notes A, B, C. The order of the events is of my choosing. Reversal of time reverses the order, and no more. There is nothing inherently impossible about the series C, B, A. Or again, the successive actions, standing, sitting, lying, can be reversed in temporal order without giving rise to a ridiculous situation. (2) On the other hand, a series of events on the macroscopic scale in causal connection cannot be so reversed without creating an obvious impossibility. I strike a match, I light the touch-paper, the rocket goes up. Reversal of this series of temporal events produces fantasy. Time-reversal in such a case destroys the causal connections; it involves the disruption of the logical links; and C, B, A, is nonsense. The original order of events was not of my choosing: it was inherent in nature itself. Nature has its own logic; which of course is not the same thing as the logic of the text-books; and it is the attempt to reverse this logic of causal connection that leads to the kind of sequence which is recognized as inherently impossible.

Now if we are right in making this distinction, time-reversal as applied to external events in general is nothing more than an amusing diversion. The real world is made of sterner stuff, and time proceeds necessarily in one direction only. If the sense of time is the subjective awareness of some basic biological change in the human organism, we must assume that the direction of that change is fixed and unalterable: birth and death occur in that order, and cannot do otherwise. If moreover the imagined reversal of the order of events in nature is recognizably fantastic, it follows that the direction of change in the external world also is fixed and immutable. In other words, our human condition is firmly linked to the order of nature; throughout which there is a single direction of change. To our subjective awareness this is the direction of time.

CAUSALITY, INFORMATION, ENTROPY

We have approached the question of the uni-directional character of time in the most obvious way by considering the logic of causal connections. However, causality is not the only category which ties up with, or appears to fix, a unique direction of temporal sequence. The matter can be approached in two other ways: from a consideration of the human mind as that which acquires and retains information about the external world; or from a study of the degradation of energy in nature. The latter introduces the well-known principle of Entropy; and this most general treatment of the uni-directional characteristic of temporal sequence will occupy the bulk of our attention in this chapter. It was the study of this aspect of nature that led Eddington[1] to coin the striking phrase, 'time's arrow'. But first of all, a few words about learning and the retention of information.

Through our senses we constantly acquire knowledge about the external world; principally through sight, but also through touch, hearing, etc. The information received by way of the several senses has that consistency which enables us to build up a rational conception of our physical environment, including

[1] A. S. Eddington, *The Nature of the Physical World*, 68.

persons other than ourselves, and their characteristic behaviour. The study of psychology suggests that all of this is retained, somewhere or somehow; though not all of it can be recalled at will by the exercise of memory. Perhaps only such information as has held our interest and attention can be so recalled. The mind also has the propensity for forgetting. Hence, while it is not true that the content of the conscious mind increases constantly as we go through life; it is true that the total quantity of stored information, memorable either at will, or through association of ideas, or by psychiatric treatment, is constantly increasing. So far as our own conscious life is concerned, the direction of increasing information is fixed. That which we remember belongs to the past, and is brought back into the conscious present. The future is unknown: strictly unknown, even though we must regard some future events (tomorrow's sunrise, our own death) as presumptively certain. Thus, the conscious mind, with its hidden store of information, and its advancing edge of knowledge, fixes for us a unique direction of time. And since we have seen already that the ordering of temporal experience is based on a subjective awareness of change within our own organism, the direction as well as a rough and ready scale of time is an immediate fact of personal knowledge: inalienable and self-evidently real for the experiencing subject. The direction of time is simply the direction of increasing information for each experiencing subject.

Well-nigh insoluble problems arise, however, once we allow ourselves to ask, How is this information stored? Scientists generally have been bemused with the working of the brain: philosophers with the working of the mind. Neither group is universally intelligible to the other. The difficulties inherent in their mutual dialogue are well brought out in a published series of broadcast talks.[1] Of the ten contributors to the symposium, only one, A. J. Ayer, seems to grasp the vital distinction between the two approaches, and to make a point of real significance. 'Mind and body', he said, 'are not to be conceived as two disparate entities between which we have to make, or find, some sort of amphibious bridge, but . . . talking about minds and talking about bodies are different ways of classifying and interpreting our experiences.'[2] The neuro-physiologist is fully

---

[1] *The Physical Basis of Mind*, ed. Peter Laslett.   [2] *loc. cit.*, 74.

entitled to postulate some mechanism for the storage of information in the brain, conceiving it as electrical or chemical according to the nature of his evidence. In so doing, he is creating a three-dimensional model which exists in time. This is his way of 'talking about bodies' in the interest of 'classifying and interpreting experience'. The philosopher's picture of mind is not tied to spatial dimensions or a material model of any kind; but he has to find room for the temporal character of experience, and the temporal nature of the store of information. Introspection, memory, the nature of attention—these are the matters which he considers in forming his conception of mental processes—his way of 'talking about minds' in the interest of 'classifying and interpreting experience'. Perhaps we can agree with Whitrow[1] when he writes, 'We should concentrate on the fact that, because brain is a material entity, it exists both in three-dimensional physical space and in time, whereas mind, as manifested in consciousness, exists only in time: it is purely a "process" and not a "thing". Consequently, the two can interact only in time, and therefore this interaction must occur mentally.' Whether therefore we fix our attention on such electrical or chemical *traces* of information as exist within the structure of the brain, or on the mental *images* corresponding to information previously acquired which are of the structure of the mind, we shall be united in identifying the unique direction of time as the direction of increasing information. Information itself is a content of the mind; though presumably it has a material analogue in the brain. And the direction of its increase in quantity is a subjective awareness of consciousness; though it is also the direction of continuing material change of a certain character in the brain. The unique direction of time is consequently related both to material reality and to subjective consciousness; and the two relationships are best seen perhaps as alternative statements of a single complex truth.

We must now exhibit the directedness of time in relation to the concept of entropy. In naming this mathematical function, the German physicist Clausius[2] went back to a Greek word

[1] G. J. Whitrow, *The Natural Philosophy of Time*, 113. I myself would question the implications of 'purely'.

[2] See C. C. Gillispie, *The Edge of Objectivity*, 399. This work contains a straightforward account of the development of the subject, avoiding unnecessary technicalities.

meaning 'transformation', so as to bring out the analogy with energy. Classical thermodynamics rests in fact on two basic principles: (1) The principle of the conservation of energy, or first law of thermodynamics; according to which energy may appear in a variety of forms (mechanical, electrical, thermal, etc.) and is convertible from one to another without loss. (2) The principle of entropy, or second law of thermodynamics; which states that in any transformation of energy from one form to another, the entropy of a system tends to increase; i.e. it may increase (and in fact generally does so), or it may remain unchanged, but it never decreases. The first law may be seen as a basic postulate of rationality, rather than as a truth experimentally established: its falsity would open the door to perpetual motion machines, which are the peculiar interest of cranks. The second law quite clearly expresses a fundamental limitation, imposed by nature itself, on the feasibility of transforming energy from one form to another completely. It stands for, or expresses, a definite trend inherent in the natural order.

It is not possible to give a precise definition of entropy itself. All that we can do is to define the change in entropy which takes place in a particular process. Imagine a substance at absolute temperature, θ.[1] While remaining effectively at this temperature, let it absorb from its surroundings an infinitesimally small quantity of thermal energy, δQ. The change in entropy, δS, is defined as the quotient, $\delta Q / \theta$. The change in entropy of a substance in any finite transformation of energy may be derived by integration: but nothing can be said about the total entropy of a substance, apart from the fact that it is essentially a positive quantity, characterizing its thermal state. The principle of entropy may be established by considering a cycle of operations carried out on a material substance, in such a manner that its temperature is changed and subsequently restored to its original value. If an imaginary cycle of operations is carried out indefinitely slowly under ideal conditions on a gas contained by a movable piston in a closed cylinder, so that the gas returns exactly to its original pressure, volume and temperature; it may be shown that the entropy of the system is unchanged at the end of the cycle. But this ideal state of affairs is possible only

[1] i.e. temperature measured from the absolute zero of temperature, which is approximately −273 degrees centigrade.

if the mechanical parts are supposed to move without friction, and if it is possible to isolate the substance perfectly from its surroundings during certain portions of the cycle. In other words, the ideal conditions presupposed by this imaginary cycle of operations are not consistent with certain awkward facts of nature itself: mechanical contrivances never move entirely without friction, and thermal insulation is never perfect. Nevertheless, such an ideal experiment is a useful theoretical device for studying certain aspects of thermal transformation.

Now let us reinstate those awkward facts of nature, previously ignored. What effect does this have on the result? Some energy is used up in overcoming friction. Some heat is lost by conduction. If these extra quantities are allowed for, the total energy of the whole system (gas, plus surroundings) is still conserved, in accordance with the first law of thermodynamics; but there is an overall increase in that elusive quantity called 'entropy', in accordance with the second law. In any real cycle, or any real process in nature, the total entropy of the system increases. In the ideal experiment, which we considered first, it would be possible to go through the entire cycle of operations in the opposite order; and apart from the direction of operation everything would be exactly the same. The cycle is said to be 'reversible'. There are no irreversible energy transformations. In the second experiment, carried out under real conditions, this is not so. Energy lost by friction is irrecoverable: heat conducted away down a temperature gradient is irrecoverable. The cycle is said to be 'irreversible'. We can therefore begin to see that nature has a kind of built-in direction, or trend; which is expressed by the law of increase of entropy.

Processes occurring in nature itself, as distinct from deliberate experiments performed under either imaginary or real conditions, are not cyclic. In principle, however, it would always be possible to complete a cycle of operations; and in consequence the second law of thermodynamics always applies.[1] The essential point is that universally in nature there is a

---

[1] Strictly speaking the laws of conservation and of entropy apply to closed, or self-contained, systems. However, a process in nature can often be treated quite legitimately as self-contained, provided sufficient of its surroundings is taken into account.

tendency for energy to be dissipated, so that it becomes less and less available for use. This is a brute fact about the physical universe as it is constituted. There is no way of getting round it. In nature, change tends to be in the one direction. This fact is sometimes expressed as a tendency to move from a state of order, to a state of disorder; from a state of organization, to a state of randomness; from a state which exhibits pattern, to a state which exhibits chaos. Suppose, for instance, that we burn oil in a furnace in order to warm a building. Initially energy is locked up in the oil, in the chemical organization of the atoms of carbon and hydrogen as molecules of the various hydro-carbons. In the furnace that energy is liberated at a high temperature: it is available for use. The water is warmed in the boiler and the pipes, and circulates round the building. But the water is never as hot as the furnace: the building is never as warm as the water. The heat we pay for disappears through the walls, even if doors and windows are kept closed; and the outside world is cooler still. Order tends towards disorder— the random motions of the colder air outside. All the energy can be accounted for indeed: none is actually lost: but it becomes progressively less and less available for subsequent use.[1] Our job, however, is not to heat public buildings; though the illustration is useful. Our job is to understand the unique-ness of the direction of time; and in particular the relation of this directedness to the phenomenon of universal increase of entropy.

The law of entropy is a different kind of statement from other laws of science. In the first place it applies only to matter in bulk, and not to individual particles such as an atom; and the reason for this is inherent in the definition of entropy change. It would be meaningless to speak of the temperature of a single atom, because temperature itself is already an average property of a large number of atoms. Entropy therefore is a statistical concept; and indeed by means of a theorem established by Boltzmann it can be expressed alternatively in terms of the statistical probability of the state of a system. Then again, the

---

[1] It is rather like the story of the cabin boy who had inadvertently dropped the captain's silver teapot overboard. Broaching the problem rather cautiously, he began by asking the captain whether a thing was lost if one knew where it was. The captain agreed that it was not: but was less convinced as the boy's logic proceeded.

law of entropy differs from other laws in the sense that it is the statement of an impossibility. It is exactly equivalent to the statement that it is impossible to convert heat into useful mechanical work by cooling the already coldest body in a system. The transformation of energy always obeys the law of equivalence; but certain kinds of transformation are either ruled out in principle, or cannot proceed to completion. This is something quite incontrovertible. In nature, change proceeds on the whole in one direction: the direction of the dissipation of available resources of energy; the direction of increasing disorder, and levelling down. Left to itself, nature grinds to a standstill. If nature has a built-in direction in this sense, manifestly there can be no time-reversal of naturally-occurring processes. The law of entropy is linked manifestly with the uniform direction of time.

We have now discerned three classes of phenomena which correlate with the direction of time: (1) causal sequences, (2) the acquirement of information, and (3) changes of entropy. Perhaps no one of these can properly be said to *fix* the direction of time. Nevertheless, it is a remarkable fact that the study of each class of phenomena *by itself* enables us to recognize a unique direction of temporal change. It is equally remarkable that the same result can be approached by way of three such apparently dissimilar lines of thought. Is it possible that there are subtle connections between causality, information, and entropy; such that we have three logically equivalent ways of stating, or fixing, the unique direction of time? This question underlies an important, but highly technical, discussion of time recently published by the French physicist de Beauregard,[1] who believes he has at any rate found the connection between entropy change and information theory. De Beauregard points out that we can obtain information about a material system only at the expense of an increase of entropy. He writes: 'nous pensons que les deux grandeurs *information* et *entropie* se transforment effectivement partiellement l'une en l'autre'.[2] Preferring to speak in terms of 'negative entropy' (i.e. entropy with the sign reversed), he postulates a scheme for a generalized

---

[1] O. Costa de Beauregard, *La Notion de Temps*, concerned largely with the theory of relativity; and *Le Second Principe de la Science du Temps*, concerned with entropy and information.   [2] *Le Second Principe*, 62.

cybernetic machine; such that a direct equivalence exists between information drawn from the environment, entropy change, and information put back into the environment in the form of external activity.[1]

'Dans la transition directe, *néguentropie → information* (qui schématise manifestement le processus de l'*observation*), le mot *information* est pris dans son acception aujourd'hui courante: *information signifie acquisition de connaissance*. Dans la transition réciproque, *imformation → néguentropie* (qui, on le devine et la suite le montrera clairement, schématise le processus de l'*action* ou de l'*organisation*), le mot *information* est pris dans son acception aristotélicienne; *information signifie pouvoir d'organisation.*'

It seems therefore that the approaches to the uniqueness of the direction of time by way of information and entropy may be regarded as virtually equivalent to one another. What can we say of the approach by way of causality?

It was pointed out many years ago that an event A, occurring at a point P, cannot be the cause of an event B, occurring at a point Q, unless the time of occurrence of A precedes that of B by at least the time taken by a light-signal to traverse the distance PQ.[2] This self-evident fact necessarily implies that effects follow their causes in temporal succession. Though the time-interval may be exceedingly small in terrestrial processes, it is none the less logically significant. For suppose that, having established a unique connection between events A and B, we were to discover that B preceded A by at least the time taken by a light-signal to traverse the distance PQ, we should conclude immediately that *B is the cause and A the effect*. The allocation of the words 'cause' and 'effect', as between a pair of connected events, is an act of the human mind, rather than a terminology given with the events themselves. The allocation is made in the light of the meanings which we associate with the two words as items of personal knowledge. I myself can cause something to happen; and it happens after I have acted—after, that is, in

---

[1] *loc. cit.*, 70–77.
[2] See, for instance, P. W. Bridgman, *The Logic of Modern Physics* (1927), New Ed. (1960), 86.

terms of my own temporal consciousness. As concepts, cause and effect are so related in the human mind that the latter follows the former in temporal succession. This is part of what the words mean. My personal knowledge of causality precedes my personal knowledge of its external effect. The moving edge of my store of information arrives at the moment of my own action before it arrives at the moment in which I discern its result in the external world. It appears therefore that the approach to the unique direction of time by way of the concept of causality is closely related to the approach by way of the increasing store of information. If this is indeed the case, the three apparently distinct approaches are logically equivalent. Any one of them serves to fix the unique direction of time. But in terms of objective physical reality, we should probably regard the argument from the principle of entropy as of primary significance.

ENTROPY AND THE CLOCK

Why do we wind the grandfather clock every Saturday evening? Because otherwise it would stop sometime on Sunday. Here is an important instance of the operation of the second law of thermodynamics which throws further light on our understanding of time.

A heavy pendulum, without driving weights, would tick merrily for a while, turning the hands of the clock. Gradually, however, the mechanical energy of the pendulum would be lost; dissipated in friction, and in creating currents in the air. The energy possessed initially by the pendulum appears as a slight warming of the surroundings: it is reduced to disordered motion. To keep the clock going, therefore, a falling weight imparts to the pendulum a small impulse once every stroke, so compensating for the energy lost. When the weight reaches the bottom of the case the clock stops: the potential energy possessed by the weight after winding has now been dissipated in disordered motion. You cannot circumvent the second law indefinitely. Replace the weights by an electric battery and a few coils of wire suitably connected. The clock will now go without winding week after week; but will stop when the battery is exhausted. No clock can go without a continuous

E

supply of energy; and this energy is steadily dissipated. Is this the connection between time and the law of entropy? Not exactly: it is only the link between the clock and the law of entropy. When the clock ceases to go, we do not say that *time* has stopped. Our own sense of time still goes on. It is the particular external change, represented by the ticking pendulum, that has come to a standstill; and is therefore of no further use for registering what we call 'time', until the weight is wound up, or a new battery is procured. The fact that the clock stops, unless continuously supplied with energy, is indeed a consequence of the law of entropy; but this is not itself the connection that we are looking for between *time* and entropy.

Something like the same argument can be repeated when we consider carefully the apparent movement of the sun as a time-keeping system. The mass involved in this case is incomparably greater than in the clock, and the rate of slowing down of the earth's rotation is consequently very small indeed. None the less it is real: the mean length of the solar day increases very slowly. In the extremely remote future, other things being equal, the earth will cease to rotate, and thereafter will always present the same face to the sun. In other words, the solar clock will stop. The movement by which we commonly register the passage of time will have ceased, and so will no longer be serviceable for that purpose. The logic of this statement is not altered at all by the fact that mankind will have perished from the face of the earth long before the rotation ceases. Once more, we have not put our finger on the actual link between time and entropy; even though it is a consequence of the general degradation of energy that the rate of revolution of the earth is a slowly decreasing quantity.

Though it is perhaps natural to look for the connection between time and entropy by considering the empirical behaviour of clocks and other time-keeping systems, are we not expecting the relation to be too direct? Are we not forgetting that time is something of which *we* are aware *subjectively*? The clock does not make time: it registers time. Clocks are no more than devices created by human ingenuity, in order that we may have available a publicly observable process of change which can express our innate sense of time. The apparent movement of the sun is a naturally-occurring process of change which serves the same purpose. But it is neither the tick of the clock, nor the daily rhythm of sunrise and sunset, that constitutes time. I was at pains to emphasize throughout the previous chapter that it is change as such within the human organism which gives us the sense of time. Basic biological change is experienced subjectively in consciousness as time. And this is the sole reason why external change, of whatever kind, can be used to register time on a scale which is usually arbitrary.

What we have to ask is this. What is the essential characteristic of the external change, manifested in any time-keeping system, which corresponds physically with the passage of time as it is given in our subjective awareness? Not surely the rhythm, which so conveniently punctuates the change, but the fact of a *decaying* motion as such. A pendulum, when not driven by falling weights or an electric battery, moves with ever *decreasing* energy. *This* is the essentially *temporal* characteristic of pendulum motion. In a properly constructed clock, this essentially temporal phenomenon is disguised: the process of decay is transferred, so to speak, to the falling weight or the electric battery. The individual swings of the pendulum, to-and-fro, have become nothing more than convenient divisions of the progressive exhaustion of the electric battery, or of the progressive dissipation of the energy of the driving weight. A stone sliding across ice has the same essential characteristic as a temporal phenomenon, coming eventually to rest as its initial kinetic energy is dissipated; but lacking the convenient division of its motion into discrete intervals.[1] Similarly the rotation of the earth is a motion in which energy is dissipated. Here too decay is the essentially temporal phenomenon. The fact that I find myself opposite to the sun once every twenty-four hours, though exceedingly convenient for time-keeping, is merely incidental to motion of this temporal character: incidental, that is, to the motion as decay, though logically connected with the motion as rotation.

Now in view of what we have said already of the law of entropy as a precise characterization of the dissipation of energy, we can see immediately what is the link between time and entropy. As ordered motion decreases, or as available

[1] The word 'interval' is used in a perfectly general sense, as a marked-off portion of something, without any temporal suggestion as such.

energy is transformed to disordered motion, entropy increases continually. The *direction* of the change in entropy marks the unique direction of time. Whether equal changes of entropy correspond to equal changes of time is a moot point.[1] What is immediately significant, however, is that our innate sense of earlier and later correlates qualitatively with a motion which is characterized physically by increasing entropy. The connection is exhibited most clearly perhaps by the state of the battery of an electrically-driven clock. The unique direction of our sense of time correlates qualitatively with the gradual exhaustion of the active chemicals which the battery contains. This gradual exhaustion is the direct consequence of the law of the increase of entropy. An electrically-driven clock, whose battery was actually charged up by the swings of the pendulum, would be a perpetual motion machine with a vengeance! Even an electrical battery which remained indefinitely in prime condition would be a contradiction of the laws of thermodynamics. The essentially temporal phenomenon of the external world, the phenomenon which correlates correctly with our own innate sense of time, is the continuing degradation or dissipation of energy, in accordance with the law of entropy. The rhythm of the clock is no more than the marking off of convenient discrete intervals of the temporal process.

ENTROPY AND THE BIOLOGICAL CLOCK

Although as yet we are unable to specify its manner of operation in detail, we have characterized the so-called biological clock as a continuing process of change within the human organism; such that the subjective experience of this change gives us the sense of time. Can we now correlate this process of continuing change directly with the law of increasing entropy? If we can,

---

[1] A mechanical clock is so designed that the energy available during each stroke of the pendulum is sufficient to overcome all losses due to friction and similar causes occurring in the course of the stroke. If the driving weight of mass m falls through a vertical height h, during a time of t seconds as measured by the clock; and if the clock is in thermal equilibrium with its surroundings at absolute temperature θ; then the energy transformed per second results in an entropy change of $mgh/t\theta$. Consequently, while it is possible to assign a constant entropy change per unit time for a particular clock at constant temperature, it is not possible to do so for clocks in general. The essential entropy-time relation is a relation in direction only.

we shall have found the essential link between entropy and time as experienced. But a word first about biological change, which in some ways is rather peculiar.

The thermodynamical theory of living systems is much less well understood than the thermodynamics of purely inanimate physical processes. It is not just that it is rather difficult to make quantitative experiments on the energy relations of a living organism; though this is true. The theoretical development of the subject is conceptually more difficult also. Anything that can be said here, though mathematically derived, is necessarily rather tentative. To begin with, a living organism is not a closed system in the thermodynamic sense. True, it is surrounded by its own skin, which marks it off from its surroundings. But we are concerned with energy relations; and the organism, though enclosed, both takes in and gives out energy. Energy is received through nourishment and solar radiation; lost through respiration and excretion, and directly through the skin, since the body temperature is usually higher than that of the surroundings. Bodily activity involves both the performance of external work (in the thermodynamic sense) and the liberation of excess heat. Clearly if we wish to treat a living organism as a closed system for purposes of calculation, we must think of it as sealed off from the outside world in a non-conducting envelope, which contains all the necessities of life and sufficient space for unrestricted movement. Manifestly in attempting to apply normal thermodynamic methods, we are creating for our investigation a somewhat hypothetical closed system.

It is possible, however, to work out a thermodynamic theory of 'open' systems, in which allowance is made for the energy and material entering and leaving; and this has been carried out in detail by Prigogine. Such systems are essentially irreversible. The theory enables us to calculate the rate of production of entropy within the space occupied by the system, and also the entropy changes in the environment. Prigogine[1] has shown that a living organism tends to a state of minimum entropy production within the volume which it occupies; and that this is achieved at the expense of an excessively high rate of

[1] I. Prigogine, *Introduction to the Thermodynamics of Irreversible Processes.* 2nd ed., 92.

increase of entropy in the environment. It has to be admitted unfortunately that a completely satisfactory test of these conclusions, experimentally a very difficult matter, is still awaited.[1] However, if this view be accepted as at least an approach to the truth, we must recognize that a living organism is similar to an inorganic non-living system to the extent that its entropy is an increasing quantity. It differs from an inorganic system to the degree that its rate of entropy increase appears to be minimal: and this fact, if established, correlates with the highly organized state of the living system. For the obvious fact of life is that an organism builds up its own ordered structure by drawing upon its environment; taking in both energy and materials, some of which are already highly organized (e.g. proteins) while others are less so. Every organism manifestly lives at the expense of lower forms of life, and in biological dependence upon its environment in general.

Now these ideas throw a flood of light upon the general character of our own biological existence, and indirectly upon the principles underlying our sense of time. Each human person takes from the environment; and by the fact of living builds up and repairs his own ordered structure at the expense of the degree of order of the total environment. Yet each one of us is to be regarded as a system whose entropy is nevertheless an increasing quantity, all through the span of life, albeit at a minimal rate. We have seen that the unidirectional trend of entropy is that property of the external world which correlates qualitatively with the unique direction of time: this is the essentially temporal characteristic. If the basic biological change, which proceeds within each one of us, is also a change involving the increase of entropy (even though at a minimum rate), we begin to see how our own innate sense of time arises. So far as its direction is concerned, from what we conceive as earlier to what we conceive as later, the correlation between time and entropy is exactly the same as for any process of change in the external world. It is presumably this qualitative agreement in direction, between internal and external change, which enables us to interpret external change as temporal; and

1 P. J. Stoward, *Nature*, **194**, 977 (1962); W. W. Forrest and D. J. Walker, *Nature*, **196**, 990 (1962).

so to register the passage of time by means of suitably chosen external processes.

But what about a quantitative link between entropy and our biological mechanism of time-keeping? Here we can go further, I believe, than in the corresponding discussion of the link between entropy and the time indication of any humanly devised clock, or naturally given scale such as the apparent movement of the sun. For the essential point now is that the basic biological change, which involves a continuing increase of entropy, is internal to us, and is experienced subjectively in consciousness. The sense of time, which each one of us undoubtedly possesses, may therefore be correlated directly with entropy increase; that is to say, with change experienced subjectively in consciousness. It appears that the entropy change of our biological functioning provides us not only with a qualitative direction for our sense of time, but also a rough and ready quantitative measure of time. Of course, it is not suggested that the experiencing subject recognizes his internal change as change of entropy: but that change which is so characterized in the language of physical science is what underlies temporality as a fact of consciousness. The picture is now as complete as we can make it in terms of objective fact and subjective experience, or in terms of scientific knowledge and personal knowledge. From the point of view of science, many details of the objective functioning of our basic biological process remain unknown. From the point of view of philosophy the distinction between objective process and subjective awareness must be sharply maintained. We have two entirely disparate ways of talking about our experience. Granted this, we are nevertheless entitled to correlate our sense of time, certainly in a qualitative and probably in a quantitative manner, with the universal fact of increase of entropy in the physical world. If we still do not know what time is, at least we have an insight as to how the sense of time arises, and why it is even as reliable as we know it to be.

ENTROPY AND THE AGE OF THE UNIVERSE

The kind of temporal statement that we make about the universe is peculiar in a number of ways. Although conceivably the universe as a whole may be subject to the law of entropy, and although it undoubtedly contains moving systems which we find serviceable for temporal reckoning, in no sense can we say that time, or time-keeping, is integral to it. The physical universe is not, and does not contain, a master clock. Time can be understood only as an item of personal knowledge. To assign a time to an external event, be it the next train or the next eclipse, is no more than a human device for the description of objective reality. Moments of time do not exist in the external world in their own right: they have no objective existence. King James', 'No bishop, no king', can be capped with, 'No observer, no time'. In so far as events in nature are expressible in temporal terms, the concept of time implied by such statements is purely relational.[1] An event is related to the clock by being observed simultaneously with it. By a process of extrapolation, events of the remote past which lie outside our immediate experience can be given a temporal reference in terms of our public scale of time. In this sense only can a statement of the age of the earth be made meaningful. We merely assign a number (of years) to what we interpret as a duration, even though there is no possible method of counting years in order to arrive at that number. The number assigned is the rough numerical solution of a mathematical equation. Such a statement of age falls into a quite different logical category, therefore, from apparently similar statements of historians. To say that Julius Caesar landed in Britain rather more than two thousand years ago is a statement based on calendrical reckoning. In principle the two thousand circuits of the earth around the sun have been counted. To say that the earth came into existence three or four thousand million years ago is not only a highly tentative statement: it belongs to a different logical class. The temporal statements of astronomers and geologists are acts of dating, in terms of our present scale of time, arrived at by highly sophisticated calculations, and their logical status must constantly be borne in mind.

In the nineteenth century considerable opposition was

[1] See, G. J. Whitrow, *The Natural Philosophy of Time*, 36–39. However, S. Alexander, in, *Space, Time and Deity*, Vol. I, 165–180, has argued against the relational view. While accepting that space and time may be treated as relational for certain purposes, he asserts that as a metaphysical account of the matter this view is inadequate (p. 174).

encountered by the law of entropy from those scientists whose materialistic outlook would not permit them to accept what appeared to be its cosmic implications. The law applies in the first instance to closed systems. Now it seems legitimate to regard the universe as a whole as constituting such a system, though admittedly an exceptional one. Such a supposition simply recognizes the fact that nothing physical exists outside the universe: consequently energy can neither enter nor leave the system. Hence it is asserted that the entropy of the universe as a whole increases steadily; which is understood as meaning that temperature differences are being slowly evened out, the whole universe tending to a dull uniformity. In Eddington's[1] phrase, the universe is 'running down'. Now entropy, as defined, is essentially a positive quantity. It is immediately apparent that a universe which is characterized by a positive entropy, increasing with time, must have had a beginning: that is to say, an original state in which the entropy was small but still positive. When that beginning took place, or what exactly it means, we are as yet in no position to suggest; but we can see already why the entropy law appeared so scandalous to the materialists of the previous century. To admit the universal validity of the law of entropy was tantamount to admitting an event of creation in some sense.

For the Christian there is no inherent difficulty in admitting an event of creation: indeed it is all too easy to jump to the conclusion that science has vindicated theology. But what is the meaning of any temporal placing of the origin of the universe? According to the accepted temporal scale, time is registered by change of some kind. A scale which is based on the movement of the earth has been extrapolated backwards to a period when the earth did not even exist. This involves an element of unreality which we can avoid only by regarding time as registered by entropy itself. Even so, the concept of a beginning of time is beset with difficulty. Time may be extrapolated backwards as long as there exists a universe, whose entropy may be conceived as registering time in a specifiable sense. If the universe came into existence in remote past time, specified in this sense (i.e. in terms of entropy), it is difficult to conceive what meaning, if any, can be assigned to any earlier time. The philosophical

[1] A. S. Eddington, *The Nature of the Physical World*, Chapter IV.

difficulty of creation *ex nihilo* is great enough: a time-scale extended back even further into a period when nothing physical existed, whose entropy change could be said to register the passage of time, is an even greater intellectual embarrassment. Probably we should be content to conceive the universe and the extrapolated time-scale as coming into existence together, in close relation to one another; and to regard this event as a kind of singular point beyond which we can push neither the laws of science nor the laws of thought. In this case, there is truth in Augustine's view that time began at the creation[1]; provided we are careful to remember the peculiar logical meaning of temporal references which fall outside all possible subjective human experience.

However, a serious objection has been raised to the whole discussion of the age of the universe in terms of the law of entropy. Although the application of the law to the universe as a whole can be made plausible, its validity is entirely dependent upon the assumption that the universe may be treated as a closed system. E. A. Milne[2] has pointed out that the proof of the second law of thermodynamics presupposes the possibility of dividing the universe into two portions: the closed system under consideration, and the rest of physical reality; in such a way that the one is not affected by processes going on in the other. This requirement, Milne asserts, is hidden from view in the usual treatment of the law. What it really amounts to is that the operator, or calculating physicist, who establishes the law of entropy, must be conceived as existing *outside* the closed system whose energy relations he investigates. If this objection can be maintained, as I think it can, then clearly the universe as a whole cannot be regarded strictly as a closed system in the thermodynamic sense, and the conclusions of the former argument become suspect. It has happened more than once that physical science has been in error through ignoring the relation between the observer and what is observed. If even theoretical problems are to be correctly formulated, without epistemological error, this relation cannot be ignored. So far,

---

[1] Augustine, *Confessions*, Bk. XI, 13. See also, E. L. Mascall, *Christian Theology and Natural Science*, 135: with further reference to the similar view of Aquinas.

[2] E. A. Milne, *Modern Cosmology and the Christian Idea of God*, 149. See also, G. J. Whitrow, *The Natural Philosophy of Time*, 7.

however, the issue has not been adequately clarified; and it is probably justifiable, as an interim position, that we should think of the entropy law as pointing in some sense to a beginning, if not of the entire physical universe then of that portion of it in which we ourselves are situated.

To sum up: entropy change appears to be the one essentially temporal characteristic of external reality. A theory of time which recognizes the law of entropy as the underlying physical basis alike of the subjective consciousness of temporality, and of temporal change in the external world, is itself a valuable contribution to our understanding. We now realize, however, that it must not be pressed to the limit. Certainly it must not be expected to provide an unambiguous answer to the question of the age of the universe: a question moreover to which we cannot assign a precise meaning in any case, in view of the logical status of the extrapolated scale of time.[1]

---

[1] In the interest of clarity we should be careful to distinguish rather sharply between two senses in which the word 'time' is commonly used. (1) The one refers to the immediate apprehensions of the self. This personal experience of time is to be described as subjective, not in the sense that it is illusory but in the sense that it belongs properly to the subject as a centre of consciousness materially embodied. (2) The other refers to the external public scale of time; however it may be provided in terms of clocks and calendars, or of the movements of the heavenly bodies. This is the time of convention, history, and science. In what sense it is to be described as real is a question to be answered by science as much as by philosophy. To the extent that clocks, calendars and heavenly bodies are objective, their temporal indications have reality for the mind which interprets them. I have argued, however, that the objective physical reality underlying both personal and public time is entropy change; of which time (in either sense) is a symbol, i.e. an immediate unanalysed subjective interpretation. This view gives unity to the whole field.

But it should be noted that while personal time, as given directly to consciousness, has both beginning and end, we are in no position to answer the question whether public time is similarly circumscribed. Public time is a fiduciary system which society at large constructs artificially for its own purposes. In so far as it is extended in either direction (before my birth, and after my death) it is the result of adding together the time-spans of succeeding generations. This extrapolated scale of time is then available for the purposes of writing history and expressing what may be known of the past and future states of the cosmos. Useful though such a scale may be, clearly there are conceptual limits inherent in the manner of its construction. Cosmology and the doctrine of creation encounter the one limit, Christian eschatology the other.

V

THE DOCTRINE OF CREATION

TRADITIONALLY the doctrine of creation has been held to give a rational account of the existence of the universe, i.e. the reason why any tangible world exists at all. The scientific view of origins is the attempt to give a rational explanation of how the universe comes to be as it is. The interests of natural science by no means coincide with those of philosophical theology: a fact which accounts for the significant difference between the two previous statements. Following the lead of the relevant passages of scripture, religious language has thought in terms of an absolute beginning of the existing world, a creation *ex nihilo*. Following the lead of Charles Darwin, natural science has consistently attempted to account for origins in terms which are broadly evolutionary: in astrophysics and biochemistry just as much as in pure biology. Both in science and in theology the discussion centres on what took place in remote periods of time: in both the idea of the beginning of the time-series presents a special problem.

Two alternative lines of approach to this complex of questions are open to us: to begin with the science and lead on to the theology, or to begin with the theology and lead on to the science. The choice will be rightly made only if we bear in mind a methodological distinction between natural science and Christian theology. Broadly speaking the sciences are capable of giving us objective facts: their proffered explanations of the facts, tentative and speculative of necessity, make no claim to touch the ultimate philosophical problem of existence as such. Herein lie both the strength and the weakness of the scientific outlook. Theology makes no claim to a direct knowledge of the objective facts: it is essentially dependent on other disciplines for the collection of relevant information. But it offers an overall interpretation of the facts, in terms of its own key concept of divinity. By and large it seems the wisest course to clarify first the interpretative scheme which theology has to offer; the way in which theology must inevitably look at these matters, if it is to be true to its own long tradition. The facts, in so far as they are known, and the theories put forward by science to explain them, can then be interpreted in theological terms. It does not follow by any means that all scientists would allow this to be a legitimate undertaking: the facts and the theories, they might say, are sufficient by themselves. From the theological standpoint, however, the procedure we have outlined is not only a legitimate approach to a group of vexed questions but a quite essential exercise in theological thinking.

THE BIBLICAL LANGUAGE OF CREATION

'A peculiar feature of Hebrew thinking is its preference for totality before details.'[1] In the scriptures the idea of creation is of altogether wider application than the origin of the cosmos: embracing also the change of 'a bad or desperate situation into a new and good one'.[2] The key to theological thinking in the Judeo-Christian tradition is therefore the recognition of a beneficent personal power, which guides the processes of nature and of history; bringing good out of evil, and calling into existence that which was not; be it Church, nation, or world. The priestly narrative of the creation, comprised in Genesis i.1–ii.3, is consequently the most highly specialized and scholarly expression of a theme which is touched on more broadly at numerous other points in the biblical literature. Though relatively late as a piece of theological writing, and expressing insights which in any case could not belong to the more primitive stages of development of Hebrew religion, its place at the very beginning of the Canon marks out its supreme importance for the understanding of the biblical message in its wholeness. If the God of Israel is not the World-Creator, he can hardly be the Lord of history in any absolute sense; and if he is not the absolute Lord of history, the scheme of salvation revealed in the scriptures can hardly be universal for all peoples

[1] T. Boman, *Church Quarterly Review*, CLXV, (1964), 149.
[2] *loc. cit.*, 148.

in all ages. The biblical claim upon us in its totality depends essentially therefore upon the theological truth of this opening passage.

Recent efforts by churchmen to vindicate the creation narrative have rightly stressed, however, that the truth of this passage does not lie in the detail in which creation is described. It is widely recognized that the priestly author could not have possessed the scientific knowledge which would enable him to portray the process with any approach to factual accuracy. Even in our day an attempt to rewrite the narrative in terms of greater scientific knowledge would still be tentative from the factual point of view: nothing of greater permanent value could be composed now than in the fifth century BC. The essence of the creation narrative does not lie in its delineation of the detail of the process. It is to be recognized rather as poetry, as a supreme expression of theological truth conveyed through the magic of words; and is to be judged accordingly. The real achievement of this priestly author is that he sees the whole order of nature and human life as something which has proceeded from the activity of God. All that exists must be interpreted in terms of the supreme Reality known to religion at its highest. That the author places himself in debt to primitive Babylonian myths is of no more significance than that Shakespeare borrowed from Danish legend and lesser dramatists. No great achievement can be judged adequately by dwelling upon its antecedents. Like all great literature, sacred or secular, the creation narrative stands in its own right, and probably for all time, as the perfect expression of what it sets out to say.

The God of the Hebrews, the only true God, is presupposed. Nowhere do we find any attempt to argue his existence in the philosophical manner: for the appeal is to what is already true in the experience of the man of religion. The creative activity of God is set before the reader as orderly and logical, the work of One who is master of the 'material' he employs. His work proceeds until a fore-ordained plan is completed, till the highest as well as the lowest forms of life have been given their existence; and at each stage that which is created is pronounced to be good: it properly fulfils the purpose for which it was intended. If the Creator is conceived anthropomorphically, it is because the author wisely adopts the only suitable analogy available to him: and perhaps he was aware that he was writing analogically. If the whole picture appears to be anthropocentric, it is not that the author held any conceit about the greatness of man, but rather that God had taken man into his confidence. Properly understood the picture is emphatically theocentric. The view of God which emerges is of One who has only to express his will and it is done. He is the centre of the picture throughout. Man, though the peak of creation, and made in the divine image, shares the kind of existence which is given to the lower orders: a representative of the sub-human world before God, and of God to the sub-human world. Not only his existence, but his due place in the created order, is assured by the theocentric character of the entire narrative.

Yet though its permanent theological and artistic value is unquestioned, and its insights must be held to be final, the creation narrative deals with matters which are beyond human understanding. The thoughtful modern reader is pulled up with a jerk by the language of the very first verse. 'In the beginning God created the heaven and the earth.' Here is language which is out of this world. Every phrase of that short sentence, the verb and each noun but the last, presents the reader with an intellectual puzzle. This is no plain, matter of fact, statement of intelligible activity: we do well to ponder the words closely. What are we to understand by *in the beginning?* What sort of a 'beginning' is this? When you and I talk about a beginning, we refer to the first point of a recognizable interval, which we choose to mark off from its immediate context for the purpose of communication. 'At the beginning of the week the weather was warm.' There was another week previous to the one I am speaking of. I stand somewhere in the middle of the temporal process. I can mark off a convenient period, and talk meaningfully about it; in full knowledge that the beginning is an arbitrarily chosen moment of time, such that I and the world already existed before this beginning. The Bible is talking about a beginning before which nothing was—except God. This does not read like a plain statement. It does not follow a normal logic of temporal sequence. It is even only remotely like the statement, 'In the beginning I was a helpless infant weighing only eight-and-a-half pounds'. Though I did not exist before that moment, others did: my existence as a new-born babe was not without antecedent causes.

Look at the next word, *God*. Though we have grown accustomed to use this queer word in the religious and theological vocabulary, it is very far from having a plain straightforward meaning. Indeed, do not we Christians tend to use it too lightly, without always sensing its mystery; thereby coming all too near to disobeying the third commandment, intellectually at any rate? Before you dare to use this word, even in repeating the first verse of the Bible, give yourself the chance to dwell on the absolute mystery which those three letters enshrine, and so often disguise. Recall to mind some of those utterly strange experiences of which scripture speaks: Jacob when he awoke from his dream, Moses at the burning bush, Isaiah receiving his call in the Temple, the Lord Jesus crying aloud in the darkness on Calvary. Remember also those moments in prayer when penitence is graciously met with forgiveness and restoration to fellowship; or those moments when you kneel to receive into your hands and heart Christ's gift of himself. Call to mind what Rudolf Otto has to say about the numinous. What *do* we mean by that short word 'God'? Philosophical theology may attempt to define and to safeguard its meaning by lists of attributes and negative propositions, but when all has been said that can be said, there it stands an absolute mystery: the unknown and unknowable behind all religious experience and all existence.

God *created*. Admittedly this verb has some slight currency outside religion and theology, which provides at least the analogical approach to its understanding. The latest creation of a Paris salon; the creative art of Beethoven: we recognize here legitimate uses of the word. To create the latest in hats is one thing: the straw and the ribbon were already in the workroom. But to transfer the word to a situation in which there is no straw and no ribbon, not an atom of anything, is a logical impropriety indeed. Perhaps this is going beyond the intention of the author of Genesis i. 'The earth was waste and void; and darkness was upon the face of the deep.' Even if today we think of creation *ex nihilo*, perhaps our author did not: there was something to begin with, something shapeless and unruly. None the less creation is a queer concept, even in the first verse of the Bible. And what about *heaven*? If the author thought of it as the blue dome, as perhaps he did, it is all of a piece with the earth; but if the word is to mean anything significant for religion, it is far from straightforward. So far then from the creation narrative telling a plain tale, it is wrestling with the deepest mystery; using a language which was never developed for any such purpose, and which is still totally inadequate. If what we read is sublime poetry, we have no right to dissect it as though it were plain prose: it is meant to evoke worship and wonder, rather than to provide easy meat for linguistic analysis. Yet at the same time it is a key passage of scripture which is saying something to us; and we are within our rights in trying to appropriate its meaning for philosophical theology. In doing so, however, we must not be insensitive to the texture of its language; nor so ham-fisted that we treat it as a plain statement of fact to be lifted out of its context without due effort of comprehension.

THE TRADITIONAL APPROACH

To explain anything is to relate it to its antecedents. The rational outlook, committed implicitly to a self-contained model of the external world and to self-contained processes of thought, is powerless to account for the ultimate origin of anything with complete intellectual satisfaction. Traditional metaphysics is nothing more than an elaborately drawn question mark.

The principle of causality enables us to explain one group of phenomena in terms of another such group, so maintaining the closed structure of reality as normally conceived. The only point at which initiative or sovereign freedom may be recognized is in the activity of the human agent. So it is that in classical philosophy and theology a cause is conceived in the first instance as a personal agent. Granted that the scientific revolution of modern times has drastically narrowed our conception of causality, it is well to remember that the concept included originally a far wider range of ideas and relationships. A human person could be the efficient cause of something precisely because he is embodied: because he has the power of moving things with his hands, and therefore to a limited degree of fashioning his environment in accordance with his own will. This is the point of departure of the classical attempt to charac-

F

terize the creative act. To postulate a First Cause, who is pure Spirit, is to employ analogy. No problem of existence, or of origins, is thereby solved, strictly speaking. When all the treatises have been written, creation remains just as much an insuperable mystery as ever. If then the problem is intellectually insoluble, and the concept of causality is employed only analogically, we must ask what is the status of the traditional form of the doctrine of creation. We remember that a distinction[1] is drawn first between necessary and contingent being. Necessary being, by definition, is that which exists of itself, without need for further explanation in terms of causality, without dependence upon any other being whatsoever. Contingent being is that which exists in a state of dependence upon being other than itself. In terms of this distinction, and by the analogical extension of the principle of causality, it is therefore said that God is the Creator of the world, in the sense that he is independent of the world's existence, being himself self-existent; while the world is created, since it exists only in a state of dependence upon God.

Now such a statement may put the whole matter in a nutshell. Its profundity is impressive, and it has its usefulness. But *what* has it *said*? In order to say anything at all about the problem of existence, it has simply postulated an existent whose existence requires no explanation. By so doing, it avoids recourse to the infinite regress to which the analogical extension of the principle of causality would otherwise commit us. So far so good. But we have no direct experience of self-existent being as such. Even God himself is not apprehended *as* self-existent being. Our knowledge of God in religion is anterior to our attempted characterization of God in philosophical theology. Religious experience, whatever else it may disclose, tells us nothing at all about distinctions of being. If we accept the traditional formulation of the doctrine, we still have the problem of identifying the postulated self-existent being of philosophical theology with the personal God who is known to us in religious experience. Is it not true therefore that what traditional theology has done is just to express the intellectual problem of the existence of the world extremely succinctly? We do not solve the problem by distinction and analogy in the meta-

---

[1] E. L. Mascall, *He Who Is*, Preface p. IX, and *passim*.

physical manner. The most we can be said to do is to express the problem with a reasonable economy of concept. The traditional doctrine of creation is a valid statement of the problem: no less and no more.

This realization, however, confers no right to belittle the achievement of traditional theology. Though the doctrine of creation is no more than a statement of the problem, it says clearly a part of what we want to say as religious men faced with the wonder of God and the unfathomable mystery of existence. *God is self-existent.* If this be so, religious experience brings us into communion with Reality which is unshakable: in whom we can put absolute confidence, to whom we can pin our faith. 'If God be for us who can be against us?' This is the proper response of man to a Reality who cannot cease to be what he is, and who has disclosed himself to the religious consciousness as perfect love. *Man exists in a state of dependence upon God.* If this be so, the givenness of earthly life falls into place. Our sense that we came into the world without our choosing; our experience of that spiritual support which can carry us through grief and temptation; the knowledge given to the man of faith that 'underneath are the everlasting arms': all these fall properly into place. We recognize that this statement of the problem rings true to our deepest experience.

If there is one criticism which can be levelled against the traditional form of the doctrine, bearing in mind the essential limitations of human thinking, it is this. It is too remote from our experience of life. It says too little. The metaphysical distinctions may be admirably adapted to convey the ultimate difference between God and the world. We may transpose them into William Temple's[1] 'equations',

$$\text{The World} - \text{God} = \text{O}$$
$$\text{God} - \text{the World} = \text{God}$$

in order to display them with greater vividness. They still say too little. Is it not true that life as we know it is a throbbing pulsating thing, full of colour, full of movement, full of change; whereas the traditional metaphysics places everything on one drab level? Self-existent being exists: what else can it do?

[1] W. Temple, *Nature, Man and God*, 435.

Contingent being exists, by divine permission: what else can it do? Of course existence is logically prior to activity. But it is in activity that interest lies. And though all divine and all human activity may be implicit in their respective modes of existence, they are hidden from view in the traditional statement of the doctrine of creation. Look again at the words we have been using: throbbing, pulsating, movement, change, activity. What do they all point to? The answer can be given in a single word: time. A proper understanding of creation in relation to time is what is lacking in the traditional approach. We can see the point of Bergson's[1] well-known protest, even if as theists we refuse to allow that evolution is itself creative.

TIME AND THE ANALOGY OF THE ARTIST

Some thirty years ago Quick[2] discussed the doctrine of creation in what was then a novel and convincing manner. His treatment does not indeed mark any departure from analogical thinking. How could it? From a strictly logical standpoint what he has to say is still a statement rather than a solution of the problem of existence. But he resolutely abandons the distinctions of being as the explicit terms of the doctrine. The metaphysics remains in the background, implicit in the specific analogies which he chooses to investigate. And what his argument loses in succinctness it gains in vividness and usefulness. What is more important, time is reinstated by a suitable choice of analogy. This, I believe, is what makes his contribution so highly significant. In what follows I lean somewhat heavily on Quick's treatment, while giving it a different slant here and there.

The analogical use of the word 'creation' is to be made more specific, more particular. Under what circumstances is the word employed in normal language? The essential idea which it always conveys is the initiation of something novel. Taking for granted the existence of the material of which something is composed (if it is a material thing) we want to draw attention to an element of newness not previously there. 'Creation' is the

---

[1] H. Bergson, *Creative Evolution*; of which the essential thesis is that change, evolutionary change, is inherent in existence as such.

[2] O. C. Quick, *Doctrines of the Creed*, 38–48.

word for the job. A new hat emerges from the Paris salon. The stuff of which it is made was there already: the hat was not. And since the hat is not identical in shape or colour with others existing previously, it is something novel. It is a new creation. And it has a creator. This is the essential idea which the vocabulary of creation exists to convey. We have direct experience of creativity in the work of the master craftsman (who does not simply copy what others have done); in the work of the artist (whatever form his art may take); in the work of the political genius (who brings into existence a new social structure). Any one of these creative activities might in principle furnish an appropriate analogy by which to express with greater vividness the relation between God and the world. If this universe could be regarded as essentially a super-mechanism, creation might be expressed adequately by the analogy of the craftsman. But organic life at every level is resistant to this kind of treatment. So far as man is concerned it is an affront to personality. Moreover, as Quick points out, the craftsman analogy implicitly suggests a finished product with which the maker has no further concern. The Christian revelation is of a God who is near at hand, deeply involved; not remote and unconcerned. If we are to find an adequate statement of the problem of existence, we need to say much more than is possible in terms of craftsmanship. Paley has been weighed and found wanting. Perhaps he never did carry much conviction except in a comfortable deistic society.

What then of the analogy of the creative artist? At once the word 'creation' springs to life. A great work of art is a creative achievement in a sense that no mechanical device, however ingenious, can be. Instead of serving a purpose. it expresses a purpose. The artist puts something of his own personality into his art. It holds the attention. It inspires wonder. In general the analogy of the creative artist has a value for theological purposes which no other can possess. The traditional metaphysical distinction of self-existent and contingent being is fully safeguarded. For we recognize that the artist exists independently of any particular work of art which he may create: whereas the work of art is dependent for its existence on the artist who creates it. We need place no undue stress upon the fact that the artist's material is found ready to hand: the creative act consists essentially in giving a new form to that material: pigments, or stone, or whatever it may be. There is no sense in which the form existed previously, except in the artistic imagination. It is the pure creation of the artist's mind.

What we have said so far is of general application to all art forms; and we have not yet touched on the question of time. Now we must become specific. Quick stresses that there are two forms of art, music and drama, where time enters into the very structure of the work. These forms differ quite fundamentally from painting and sculpture. A painting can be looked at for just as long as we please: in a sense it can be taken in at a single glance, though further time and attention reveal greater richness of content. Though it exists in time, and can be fully appreciated only in time, time is not of its essence. It is static, not dynamic. By contrast a musical composition cannot be appreciated in a shorter time than it takes to perform. To the extent that the performance is repeatable (exactly so, only in a recording) attention can be given to individual details at different times; somewhat as attention may be given to the detail of a picture in the observer's own time. To assert this, however, tends to obscure the fact that in a specific manner time is of the essence of the musical composition. The picture is a created pattern in space: the music a created pattern in time. We can appreciate a spatial pattern by momentary attention to it, at least to a degree. We cannot appreciate a temporal pattern by a corresponding momentary attention; for only a fraction of it can be before the mind in any one moment.

A pattern in time implies change and development; beginning and end. How much nearer to life in its fulness than any static art, however great! If now we shift our attention from music to drama, temporal structure takes on added significance. The pattern in time becomes more meaningful; consisting not of musical phrases but of human actions and speech. The development, now a plot, reflects a typical human situation; portrays real human problems; is governed by real human attitudes. Yet behind it stands the human dramatist whose creation it is, in whose mind it took shape. Not only is the drama as a whole dependent upon the dramatist, but every character within it is given life by him. As in real life, time serves for the working out of the plot, for the development of individual characters, for the articulation of motive and action with realistic logic, for the disclosing of meaning in a temporal situation. All is creation; all is under the control of the dramatist-creator. A limited degree of free-will is creatively given to the players, which they exercise interpretatively in the performance. It has even been said that the characters themselves, as they form in the artist's mind, acquire a certain autonomy of their own, which imparts to the temporal process of the play an authentic quality.

The search for a specific creator-analogy, which shall be fully adequate, has led us first to the arts and finally to the drama, in which time is given its due significance. The relation of the Creator to his creation, while remaining a mystery, is represented analogically by the relation of the dramatist to the drama. Self-existence and contingency are preserved within the limits of the analogy. Temporal reality is reproduced, and the sense of purpose safeguarded, in dramatic creation. True, no problem is solved: the dramatist analogy contains nothing more than a statement of the problem of existence. Underwritten implicitly by the traditional metaphysics, it none the less marks a step forward in human thinking.

The very idea of creation *ex nihilo* remains a logical impropriety. To follow Ramsey's[1] method of dealing with such impropriety, we may make the first verse of Genesis meaningful somewhat like this. I know what it means to create a new hat, though the stuff exists already. I know what it means to create a painting, though pigments and canvas exist already. I know what it means to create a symphony, though nothing but the possibility of making certain noises on instruments exists already. I know what it means to create a drama, though nothing but an inside knowledge of human nature is given. Here is a series of terms pointing to, but not leading to, what it means to create a universe when nothing exists already. The logical jump across the infinite gap, to where the series points, is the religious response to the totally unintelligible fact that the universe exists and I exist in it. Creation is the model: *ex nihilo* the qualifier. Put the two together in the light of the analogy which has been developed, and we come as near as we ever can to understanding the sentence, 'In the beginning God

---

[1] I. T. Ramsey, *Religious Language*, 71–75.

created the heaven and the earth.' But all we have done is to embroider the classical statement of the problem of existence by fixing attention on specific analogies. The logical jump from analogy to reality is simply the measure of our failure to comprehend. Mystery remains unsolved.

THE PRINCIPLE OF INTERPRETATION

In the next two chapters we are to take a look at some of the facts and theories about the origin of the universe and of organic life, which come to us in the name of science. What is to be our attitude to these facts and theories? How are we to interpret them?

It is not for the theologian or the philosopher to question ascertained facts. The business of modern science is a highly specialized undertaking. Few theologians either have any first-hand acquaintance with its methods, or are in a position to assess for themselves the reliability of its conclusions. Admittedly scientists, being human, can make mistakes; but it is their own business to rectify them once made. The only intelligent, and indeed humble, course is to accept without question what scientists have to tell us about their own specialized studies; asking merely that ascertained fact and tentative speculation be clearly distinguished in the more or less popular communications on which most of us rely. If scientific theories and opinions stand in need of revision, let us wait till scientists revise them. The scientific account of origins must therefore be accepted as the nearest approach yet available to the truth in these matters. The job of philosophical theology is to interpret these facts and theories, tentative though some of the latter may be, in terms of its own key-category, belief in God.

Interpretation can be thought of as the translation of scientific statements into the richer language of theism. It is not an alternative to scientific explanation, but its complement. What we have to do is to relate the current scientific views of the origin of the universe and of organic life, without loss of content, to the view of ultimate reality to which our Christian faith commits us, also without loss of content. The task cannot be accomplished without tensions: the growing pains of human understanding. It is better that the tensions should be felt within the discipline of theology, rather than between theologians and scientists as once was the case. As men of faith we have to accept new ways of thinking about the works of God, while remaining true to God himself. The hitherto unsuspected immensity of the universe, the part apparently played by random process, the strange story of evolution: these and many other details of the scientific world-view are to be integrated into the outlook of Christian theology by a venture of faith. To attempt the task at all expresses the most profound faith in God himself: to remain behind the Maginot line of the traditionalist outlook betrays a lack of faith at the deepest level.

The future of Christian theology is for those who dare to venture forth into the unknown. In the faith that God as World-Creator and Lord of history has used, and still uses, the strangest of instruments in the achievement of his purpose, we can live with the tensions, we can be led to deeper understanding. What we have to do is to claim the facts of science, even the most tentative of its theories, for God; and humbly to believe that he who has created all things has the wisdom to guide all process to the fulfilment of his purpose.

VI

THE CHRISTIAN AND THE COSMOS

LOGICALLY I suppose, an account of the origin of the universe should precede any discussion of the evolution of living forms. As so often happens however, historical development in this enormous field has not followed logical order. Nor is this surprising: for the general picture of evolution in the organic world was able to take shape in a period when astronomy was still involved in what might be called the preliminary observational task of surveying the heavens. The fruitful partnership of astronomy and atomic physics, and the development of instruments capable of collecting information from the remotest regions of space, on which an understanding of the origin of the universe essentially depends, belong to a relatively recent period of scientific investigation. Accordingly, cosmology has tended to lag behind evolutionary theory in the biological field; and in the event cross-fertilization between different disciplines has led to the adaption of the evolutionary idea for cosmological purposes. In this chapter, where we are concerned solely with the world of inorganic matter, a certain looseness in the use of the word 'evolution' must be accepted as inevitable outside its proper context. Without attempting anything like a complete account of the present state of cosmological theory, I shall merely touch upon some of the key ideas in terms of which scientists have sought to explain the general constitution of the physical universe. Thus we shall glimpse a continuing process in time, raising again the questions of the age of the solar system and of the universe itself. But the real job in hand is the interpretation of the temporal process of world-formation in theological categories. Cosmological details are of interest here only in so far as they serve this purpose.

A word of warning is apposite at this point. The general run of popular expositions of the present state of cosmology neither distinguish with sufficient care between fact and theory, nor indicate at all clearly the essential limitations under which science labours in this particular field of study.[1] Any theory which attempts to account for the present state of the universe is based upon observation, rather than on *experiment* and observation. The essence of the experimental method, available elsewhere in scientific work, is that relevant external conditions can be manipulated at will by the investigator, who then observes the effect of such variation on the phenomenon in question. In a certain sense the experimental method enables us to put specific questions to nature. The answers which nature gives provide a crucial test of our theories. Though it is not possible strictly speaking to verify a particular theory by experiment, at least it is possible to demonstrate its falsity, or in certain cases its inadequacy. In astrophysical investigations the complexity of the apparatus used for the gathering of information may well obscure from the public mind the handicap under which cosmologists work. All that the investigator can vary is the character of the observations he chooses to make: the spectra of stars, the shapes of remote galaxies, the radio-waves from particular regions of the sky, etc. He is in the same logical position as a detective collecting clues. Hence cosmology must proceed in two stages: (1) to suggest model universes consistent with the general laws of nature as far as they are known; (2) to accept as a working theory that model which accounts for the greatest number of observed facts with the greatest economy of *ad hoc* hypothesis. As in a strictly experimental science new observations may invalidate previously useful theories; but in the absence of the power of manipulation the investigator can only *wait* for the observations. He cannot force the pace. Consequently the state of the subject is highly tentative; and accepted views become outdated more rapidly than in almost any other branch of science.

The second important limitation imposed upon cosmological studies arises from the fact that light and radio signals take a considerable time to travel from an astronomical object to the

[1] G. C. McVittie, *Fact and Theory in Cosmology*, is a notable exception in this regard; and in spite of some mathematical sections can be commended to the general reader.

observer: eight minutes from the sun, three years from the nearest fixed star, perhaps a thousand-million years from the most distant visible galaxies. No information travels faster than an electro-magnetic wave. It is therefore impossible to obtain any information more 'up-to-date' than a light or radio wave can carry. The common-sense way of expressing this limitation would be to say that we do not see the whole universe as it is at this moment. Every astronomical object is seen only as it was when the light which we observe left it. The further the object, the more 'out-of-date' our information. There are objections, however, to this common-sense view. On epistemological grounds we ought to examine the meaning of the phrase, 'the present state', as applied to a distant object; and to do so we should recognize the relativity of all temporal perception. Shelving such questions for the present, we realise that we are somewhat in the position of a blind man who has to form a theory of his physical environment on the basis of the sounds he hears. He hears the thunder, but has not seen the lightning. How is he to know how far away the storm is? Astrophysics suffers from a handicap of this character. The estimation of distance becomes a highly sophisticated but somewhat uncertain undertaking. It is never possible to determine with precision the distance of an astronomical object more remote than the nearest fixed stars. All that is possible is to interpret some peculiarity of the radiation received from such an object in terms of distance; and clearly changes in theory and changes in estimated distance are mutually related. If we are inclined to be impatient with the constant revision of the figures quoted by astronomers, we should remember the analogy of the blind man.

AGREEMENT AND DISCORD IN COSMOLOGY

Underlying the wide diversity of cosmological speculation certain generally accepted ideas command our attention first of all. On the scale of the universe as a whole, the galaxies, of which our own Milky Way system is one, are regarded as the natural units of organization. Their number is immense; and their optical spectra show a characteristic red-shift, which is greater the more faint the galaxy. It is natural to interpret the

red-shift as a Doppler effect[1]; on the assumption that recognized spectra correspond to the same chemical elements as in
terrestrial experiments. This leads to the conclusion that all the
galaxies are receding, at velocities which increase with increasing distance. Hubble's law, based on the best observations
available, states that the rate of recession of a galaxy is in direct
proportion to its distance from the observer. The obvious
implication of this discovery is the expansion of the universe, a
fact which has been recognized now for about thirty years.

Although the matter contained in the universe appears to be
concentrated almost entirely in the galaxies themselves, whose
separations greatly exceed their own dimensions, it is usual for
general cosmological purposes to postulate a model universe in
which the distribution of matter is uniform in the large; and
this procedure is held to be justified by the scale of the universe
and the immense number of galactic systems. If then hypothetical observers be supposed stationed at various points in the
universe, all such observers must be regarded as equivalent to
one another: none is in a privileged position; all see the same
sequence of 'world-pictures' in the large. This generally
accepted postulate, known as the cosmological principle,[2]
underlies all particular solutions of the problem which have
been proposed. It is well to be clear at the outset what kind of
simplification is imposed upon the general problem in order to
make it amenable to mathematical treatment. The model
universes of general cosmology are smoothed out models of the
actual universe. Their construction would be an impossible
task otherwise. For theoretical purposes therefore the problem
has been reduced to the setting up of a mathematical characterization of a material fluid, constantly expanding, which is
the totality of things. From this point onwards, we need only
observe that possible solutions of the problem fall into two main
groups. The differences between these groups of cosmological
theories are significant for theology; the variety within each
group need not concern us. Fortunately for the general reader,
who wishes to keep abreast, the more important characteristics

[1] Change of apparent frequency due to motion of the source. Cf. the whistle of
a moving locomotive as heard by a stationary observer.

[2] McVittie, *loc. cit.*, 91; and W. H. McCrea, *Reports on Progress in Physics,*
Vol. XVI, 326 f.

of the two types of theory have been presented in broadcast talks which have since been published.

The so-called evolutionary theories, popularized by Lovell,[1] conceive the universe as finite, both in time and space. The world-model proposed usually starts from a highly compressed initial stage, the 'primeval super-atom' of Lemaître, which contains all the material and all the energy that exists. From this beginning the universe is in a state of constant expansion, continuously thinning out; and its present observable limits suggest that its age is to be reckoned as some thousands of millions of years. The general picture is more or less consistent with the views to which we were led by a consideration of the law of entropy, assuming this law to be applicable to the universe as a whole. The evolutionary theories point back to a definite origin of the universe, an event of creation, which precedes in time all the progressive changes leading up to the present state of the cosmos.

The other important group comprises the steady-state theories, popularized some time ago by Hoyle,[2] and since then modified somewhat in detail. The essential difference between these and the theories previously mentioned is that the cosmological principle is widened so as to include the postulate that the universe is uniform in the large in time as well as in space. The so-called 'perfect cosmological principle' implies that the universe is in a steady state; infinite in time and, on account of its continuous expansion, infinite in space. It has neither beginning nor end in time; nor spatial limits. The apparent limits of the visible universe are held to be a consequence of the fact that at sufficiently great distances the rate of recession approaches the velocity of light. A further implication of the perfect cosmological principle is that the universe is not thinning out in time. Instead, the theory postulates a process of continuous creation of new matter, randomly throughout the universe, at a rate exactly sufficient to balance the outward expansion and so to keep the average density constant. The required rate of creation turns out to be far too small for direct observation of this phenomenon to be possible. The familiar concept of an origin finds no place in this view of the universe;

[1] A. C. B. Lovell, *The Individual and the Universe* (Reith Lectures, 1958).
[2] F. Hoyle, *The Nature of the Universe.*

yet the essential logical function of an origin is in some sense preserved by the novel hypothesis of continuous creation.

It goes without saying, since both groups of theories have their exponents, that at present there is no way of deciding between their rival claims to represent the facts in broad outline. Radically different though they are in their basic postulates, each gives as good an account as the other of the observed state of the universe. It is conceivable that the question may be settled by the relatively new technique of radio-astronomy, since observation of the most remote regions of the universe is equivalent to observation of the universe as it existed in remote periods of time; and it may be possible to determine whether or not the universe is thinning out. As yet it is too early to say. Whichever view is accepted as the best over-all representation of the universe as a whole, there is more general agreement regarding the origin of astronomical objects within the system. Random motion and gravitational attraction lead to the formation of spiralling galaxies, and to the genesis and subsequent growth of stars. Enormous supplies of energy are available from various nuclear reactions; so accounting both for the brightness of the stars and the thermal origin of the whole range of chemical elements, either in the explosions of super-novae or perhaps more slowly in the densest regions of the other stars, or quasi-stellar objects. The origin of planetary systems has been variously explained, and many a promising theory has been falsified by the recognition of some peculiarity of the solar system. Evidence for the origin of the earth is available from geophysical studies as well as from general cosmological considerations. There is now fairly wide agreement that the earth began its history as an agglomeration of solid particles; and several lines of argument point to an age of the order of three or four thousand-million years. Our aim here is to interpret this array of facts and partially conflicting cosmological theories in terms of the Christian doctrine of creation. The prospect is exciting, even though the tensions may not all be resolvable.

COSMOLOGY AND CREATION

The mere extent of the material universe, in space as in time, though an obsession and even a stumbling-block to some individuals, is of comparatively little theological significance: except in so far as it pricks the bubble of human conceit. The point of real interest, in view of earlier scientific attitudes, is the way in which the word 'creation' has crept into the cosmological vocabulary during the middle decades of the century. Of course the use of a word can be deceptive. The word was ready to hand in the language, and it has proved itself useful in the newer developments in cosmology. The important question, however, is the exact meaning which has become attached to the word in its scientific use. Is its content the same as in philosophical theology? This question will repay closer attention.

The essentially new situation in cosmology, which has led to the use of 'creation' as a scientific category of thought, is the discovery of the expansion of the universe in accordance with Hubble's law. Previously the universe was looked upon as static: it contained motion indeed, but it was thought of as of fixed extent in space. That view has been replaced: the universe is looked upon now as dynamic. The attempt to characterize this dynamic view of the universe has led to the recognition of two possible kinds of theory in cosmology. The logical possibilities are in fact limited to these two contrasted groups of cosmological theories. *Either*, the total quantity of matter contained in the universe is constant; and expansion therefore implies necessarily a continuing diminution in the average density of matter in the course of time. *Or*, the average density of matter is constant in time; and this in turn implies an unexplained process by which new matter appears constantly within the universe, so compensating for the effect of expansion. In view of all previous developments in scientific thinking, it is indeed somewhat surprising that this second logical possibility should have been taken seriously. That it should have been so taken is attributable to the fact that the so-called perfect cosmological principle has a conceptual tidiness, which appeals to the mind that seeks for wide unifying principles of great generality. Both logical possibilities have therefore been explored. In the one case, the equations of the evolutionary models must include a boundary condition in time; such that they represent the state of the universe at later times, but are physically meaningless at earlier times. The time in question is the moment in the remote past at which the universe as we know it can be said to have begun its existence: that is to say, the moment of creation. In the other case, the equations of the steady-state models must contain a term which allows for the spontaneous occurrence of new matter at a definite rate in time: that is to say, for continuous creation. Whichever way the problem is tackled, 'creation' simply denotes the empirical occurrence of matter, previously non-existent in any physical sense: i.e. 'creation' is something not amenable to scientific explanation in terms of antecedent phenomenal conditions. As an abrogation of the principle of the conservation of mass, previously accepted as self-evident, it is indeed something of a scandal to the scientific mind. But science must be true to what is observed; even though this means the repudiation of ideas formerly accepted. Hubble's law of expansion has made the postulate of creation in this empirical sense a logical necessity of modern science.

For theology on the other hand, the significant point is the relation of the creative event to the Creator: a question which lies outside the purview of cosmology. The mere occurrence of new matter, either in remote past time or continuously at all times, without antecedent phenomenal cause, is an apparent irrationality positively demanding integration into a larger world-view. Christian theology therefore takes up the problem of origins exactly at the point where natural science lays it down; accepting what scientists have to contribute from their own expertise, and interpreting this contribution theistically. 'Creation', as understood in philosophical theology, is the act of God by which contingent being is brought into existence. It does not just happen, spontaneously and irrationally: it is willed. Following the line of thought developed in the previous chapter, the creative act can be represented usefully in terms of the analogy of the dramatist. Material creation is then seen as the preliminary stage of a cosmic drama; the later stages of which include organic life, the human race, and the 'new creation' in Christ. Thus, to the question whether cosmologists and theologians mean the same thing by the word 'creation', which their respective vocabularies share in common, the answer is now apparent. They do not. There is an area of contact between the two uses of the word, but that is all: and

G

it may even be that this overlapping of concepts is more a hindrance to mutual understanding than a help.

At this point we may usefully enquire whether either of the main theories of cosmology is more amenable to theological interpretation than the other. On the face of it, the evolutionary view appears to accord more readily with the traditional Christian teaching of a single creative act 'in the beginning'. In that it allows physical meaning to the concept of time only after the moment in which the universe may be thought to have originated, it may seem also to corroborate the theological view, previously mentioned and traceable to Augustine, that the universe was created with time rather than in time. If the evolutionary models eventually gain acceptance among cosmologists, this point of agreement might go some way towards clarifying the accepted concept of time: at least in its application to objective observable process. However, it would be a mistake to place undue emphasis on this superficial agreement: certainly it must not be allowed to dictate any preference in cosmological theory. On the other hand, the steady-state models, with their postulate of continuous creation, may be held at least to illustrate the continuing activity of God. This too has the appearance of a superficial agreement between science and theology; which again must not be over-emphasized. But clearly, whichever view may be found to represent the scientific truth of the matter, when the issue has been decided, the theological contribution to our understanding of the cosmos is the same: the insistence that creation is the work of the Creator. All that exists, whenever it came into existence, owes its existence to an act of the creative will. Moreover, at this stage of human understanding, it is of no great significance to theology whether the universe is conceived as finite or infinite, either in time or in space.[1]

To resume the main line of the argument. Material creation is the first stage of the cosmic drama. Reference to a first stage implies the recognition of subsequent stages. Reference to creation implies the recognition of purpose. Novelty is of the essence of the creative act: each subsequent stage in the cosmic process exhibits novelty and expresses purpose. To the human intelligence the creation of matter *ex nihilo* is no doubt the most

[1] See Chapters IX and X.

striking instance of creative activity: it is by no means the most significant, when we bear in mind the continuing initiation of novelty throughout the cosmos, and recognize this as an expression of divine purpose. Thus. in our theological interpretation of the facts and theories of modern science, we shall be justified in speaking of creation in the broader sense with reference to the emergence of each galaxy, each star, each planet. The emergence of each new configuration of previously existing matter can be explained of course in general terms by cosmological theory. But the laws of nature with which cosmology operates are the laws imposed by God on his creation; laws which our minds express in mathematical and logical form. If their continuing operation leads to the emergence of the various classes of astronomical object, then the occurrence of these objects in temporal process may be seen as creatively willed by God, either generally or specifically. The operation of what science regards as random processes in accordance with fundamental laws must not blind us to the continuing operation of divine providence; even though the discoveries of modern science require us to enlarge enormously our conception of the manner in which the divine will controls the natural order. There is some degree of tension between the concept of randomness and that of purpose or providence: this is one of the tensions we must live with. Living with it, we learn to see that cosmic randomness on such a vast scale in time and space of necessity leads to the emergence of those configurations of matter (galaxies, stars, and planets) which make possible the higher levels of organization, and human life in particular. It is not for us to question the feasibility of the divine plan; still less its wisdom. Rather it is for theology to recognize that the eventual emergence of habitable planets is logically inherent in a cosmos which is characterized equally by the existence of randomness and the operation of fundamental law on a sufficiently large scale: and having recognized this truth, the contribution of theologians is to continue to interpret each stage in the cosmic process by the category of creation. Only so can we strike a balance between process and purpose: only so do we remain faithful to our deepest insight.

In particular we are justified in speaking of the creation of the solar system, and of the earth which we inhabit. This instance will be considered in detail, in view of its significance for human life; and thereby we shall bring out more clearly the relation between scientific and theological thinking on the subject of origins. How far is it possible to give a scientific explanation of the existence of the solar system? The sun is a modest-sized member of the class of main-sequence stars. Cosmological theory can account reasonably well for the genesis and subsequent development of such stars. So far, so good. But how does this sun come to have a planetary system in the space surrounding it? Maybe planetary systems are relatively common. Many cosmologists are of the opinion that an enormous number of stars have planetary systems; that the solar system is in no way unique; but we do not know. There are many uncertainties however regarding the origin of such systems.[1] The older view that the near passage of another star (a chance occurrence) caused a tidal wave on the sun, which broke away and separated into a series of planets, fails to account for the fact that the chemical composition of the planets differs widely from that of the sun. The newer view that the planets are aggregates of cosmic matter, swept up into the gravitational field of the sun, allows for the difference in composition, but does not by itself explain the origin of cosmic material consisting principally of the heavier elements. Possibly these materials result from the explosion of a super-nova; either a star which was formerly a near companion of the sun, or one through whose debris the sun travelled at some time. Whatever the final solution of the problem, chance is a principal ingredient in the scientific account of origins.

In view of these uncertainties, and the part played by random process, we must be careful not to invoke the idea of the creation of the solar system as an *alternative* to a complete scientific explanation. It is not the job of theology to patch up the holes in our scientific knowledge. Even though we do not know, and may never know, exactly how the solar system originated, we must assume that a valid scientific explanation is possible in principle: i.e. that the event was the result of antecedent phenomenal causes, which from the point of view of science constitute its full explanation. The job of theology is to interpret the same facts in theistic terms. Thus in speaking

[1] W. H. McCrea, *Contemporary Physics*, Vol. IV, 278–290.

of the creation of the solar system, we hold at one and the same time that its origin is physically explicable and also divinely purposed. There can be no antithesis between creation as theology understands it, and explanation as science understands it. The two aspects of truth are to be seen as complementary.

The creation of the solar system, understood in this sense, marks a significant stage in the process leading up to the creation of man; and we are entitled to think of this particular planet (suitable on grounds of chemical composition, size, and distance from the sun, for the development of organic life) as being created in order that it might be inhabited by our race. Modern cosmology gives no ground for supposing this earth to be unique, however. The possibility that other inhabited planets may exist elsewhere in the cosmos, while purely speculative, has already exercised the minds of theologians, who have previously thought of the human race as a unique creation. The explicit difficulty is not so much that man is dethroned from his presumed pre-eminence, as that we are required to take a somewhat wider view of the Incarnation in relation to the whole cosmos. This is a matter of psychological adjustment rather than of theological revision. If other 'human races' exist, we cannot ignore the possibility of the need for redemption in other worlds; for we cannot shelter behind the supposition that the Fall is a peculiarly terrestrial occurrence. How is the need to be met? By other Incarnations elsewhere? Or by the communication to other 'human races' of the benefits of the one Incarnation which we know? The latter suggestion is scarcely realistic, and would seem to place undue missionary responsibility upon the inhabitants of the earth! The former suggestion at first sight appears to deny the uniqueness of our Lord Jesus Christ. Second thoughts will show this impression to rest upon a misapprehension of classical doctrine. To quote *Quicunque Vult*, Christ is 'One, not by the conversion of the Godhead into flesh, but by taking of the Manhood into God'. It is remarkable, to say the least, that orthodox belief, formulated in the patristic age, leaves room for other Incarnations in other 'human races', if such exist, without detracting from the uniqueness of the Incarnation which we know for the salvation of our own race. Since the patristic age can have had no inkling of the problem under discussion, it is apparent (I think) that the way has been left open in orthodox theology by the realistic humanism and true humility which speaks of a 'taking up of the Manhood' rather than of a 'conversion of the Godhead'. Of course the problem of the salvation of other 'human races' is hypothetical to a degree: it must be faced however, if we are even to entertain the view that our own humanity may not be entirely unique.

Thus a tolerably clear picture is emerging of the creative process in the universe as a whole. While still liable to much revision in detail, the broad outlines of what is possible as well as the scale of cosmic phenomena are reasonably well understood. The scientific evidence discloses a universe which is essentially temporal in character. It is subject to continuing change; indeed such change is inherent in it. In scientific theory the cosmic process is represented in the only way possible: in terms of the public scale of time, with all the attendant ambiguities already discussed in Chapter IV. In theological interpretation we think rather of the drama of creation, and of God as the Master Dramatist; since we recognize now that time (or better, temporality) is inherent in the creative process at all levels, and that the recurrence of novelty (leading to higher forms of organization) can be understood only in terms of purpose. Vast extents of time are necessary for the operation of random process: vast tracts of space for the accommodation of by far the greater part of created matter, which apparently never ascends far in the hierarchy of organization. We may speak legitimately of the 'creativeness of the random element', in accordance with fundamental laws and the logic of statistical process. But what we mean is that, from the stand-point of Christian theism, such process is to be interpreted not as 'blind chance' but as the working out of divine purpose in a manner hitherto unsuspected either by scientists or theologians. The picture is taking shape; and in spite of the tensions which its acceptance entails, we claim it as the creative activity of God.

A CRITIQUE OF POSITIVISM

We remarked earlier that many scientists would regard the theistic interpretation of their own discoveries and theories as a totally unnecessary, even as a mistaken programme. In this the scientific fraternity would have a good deal of support from that modern school of philosophy which, beginning with logical positivism, has developed the weapon of linguistic analysis against the traditional forms of religious and theological utterance. It will be remembered that Flew[1] developed his parable of the Invisible Gardener with just this purpose in mind. What began as an attack however, has become an entirely helpful enquiry; whose present purpose is the elucidation of the meaning which undoubtedly underlies traditional theological assertions. With the linguistic analysts we must therefore ask, What would count for or against the concept of divine creation as a legitimate interpretation of the facts and theories of cosmology?

We can admit right away that there is no test, which can be applied in practice, capable of validating or falsifying the assertion that 'God is the Creator of all that exists'. For the subject of this statement, God, though identified for theological purposes as the ultimate Ground of all being, is non-objective; that is to say he cannot be known directly and incontrovertibly through sense experience which can be shared. The attempt to apply a positivist verification principle is an altogether too clumsy way to establish either the meaning or the legitimacy of such an assertion, however. As Crombie[2] has pointed out, the test of meaning and legitimacy involves the application of two stipulations to the assertion in question. He writes, 'The first is a logical stipulation, and it is to the effect that nothing can be a statement of fact if it is untestable in the sense that the notion of testing it is precluded by correctly interpreting it. The second is a communicational stipulation, and it is to the effect that nobody can fully understand a statement, unless he has a fair idea how a situation about which it was true would differ from a situation about which it was false,'. The assertion that God is Creator is not precluded from being a factual statement by the first stipulation. It is not *logically* untestable; though no man is in the position to test it. Consequently it is not meaningless: it is factual, by intention and in construction. Is it a legitimate statement? That is to say, can it be held as factually

[1] Antony Flew, in *New Essays in Philosophical Theology*, 96.
[2] I. M. Crombie, in *New Essays*, 125 f.

true? To assert its factual truth as an item of communication, according to the second stipulation, we must at least have an idea of how a world created by God would differ from one not so created. And we have. If God has the character revealed in the New Testament, a world of which he is the Creator would be one in which it was possible to interpret human experience in its wholeness as meaningful; whereas a world of which he is not the Creator would be one in which human experience is 'a tale told by an idiot . . . signifying nothing'. We are not required to prove that life is meaningful: it is sufficient that we should know how meaning differs from unmeaning. Knowing this, we are entitled to say that human life is meaningful and that God is Creator. And in so saying we make an assertion which passes all legitimate tests of logic and communication, short of factual proof.

What then is the status of the assertion that 'God is the Creator of all that exists', when this assertion is made in the context of modern cosmology? It is a factual statement not yet proved. 'Not yet proved' implies that proof is not impossible logically, or in principle. Proof is necessarily deferred, so the Christian holds, until after death, when we shall know as we are known. At present the assertion is therefore an expression of faith: we speak from faith to faith. To assert the creatorship of God is the traditional Christian expression of the attitude which we take up when we say that the universe is not meaningless. In the context of modern cosmology this assertion is the claim that we detect meaning even in processes which science can treat only as random and statistical; because we recognize that the operation of such processes through sufficiently long periods of time has in fact led to the organizational level which makes human life a possibility, and human life has meaning.

How does it come about that the Christian theologian stands by such an assertion? Briefly, because he lives within the historic Christian community, sharing in its experience of grace and fellowship. The assertion that God is Creator is a cardinal point of the Christian creed. Its acceptance as factually true is part of the meaning of being a Christian. In the face of criticism from without, however, we readily concede the truth of the four following propositions: (1) Experience of life, including specifically Christian experience, helps to form the conviction that God is Creator. (2) Experience nevertheless cannot prove the factual truth of this assertion during earthly life. (3) Experience of life, especially a succession of misfortunes judged to be unmerited, may shake the conviction; but for no logical reason, since it is an article of faith that the love of God is sometimes expressed in severity. (4) Experience can never disprove the assertion that God is Creator.

It seems therefore that the conviction that 'God is the Creator of all that exists' is what Hare[1] calls a *blik*. There is no external objective test which counts either for or against it. It is held as an integral part of a total attitude. It supplies the natural principle of interpretation, to be applied to all experience, by the person whose *blik* it is. It is logically unassailable. Equally it cannot be established on the basis of anything more fundamental. As Hare remarks however, 'without a *blik* there can be no explanation; for it is by our *bliks* that we decide what is and what is not an explanation'. The *blik* that God is Creator is for the Christian the basis of any 'explanation' of the universe which he is prepared to entertain. He is well aware that not all his fellow men will agree, but he sticks his neck out, and expresses his conviction that the universe for all its randomness is not without meaning. The analogy of the dramatist displays the creation-concept as the meaningfulness of temporal process throughout the cosmos: and herein lies its strength. But what from the strictly logical point of view is personal interpretation remains the firm conviction of the Christian. In other words we interpret the universe in this sense precisely because we believe this to be the ultimate truth about it. What positivism calls a *blik* is a Christian insight, into the structure and meaning of reality.

[1] R. M. Hare, *New Essays*, 100 f.

VII

EVOLUTION AND CHRISTIANITY

BOTH science and theology have made notable advances since that stormy meeting of the British Association when Huxley and Wilberforce confronted one another over the theory of natural selection, recently put forward by Darwin. The legend has tended to portray the one protagonist as upholding the facts of science with dignity, the other as a purblind adherent of traditional views who was not above using scorn and abuse in order to maintain his position. Yet in Wilberforce's favour it should not be forgotten that his classic review[1] of *The Origin of Species* showed an open-mindness towards new knowledge, which went as far as could be expected under the circumstances. And although the conflict between the mechanist in biology and the fundamentalist in religion is still inclined to flare up, generating unnecessary heat, broadly it is true that theology has adjusted itself to many aspects of evolutionary thinking; while biology has both deepened its knowledge and abandoned something of its former aggressiveness. Further study has shown the inadequacy of natural selection by itself to account for the evolutionary process. Without the raw material of novelty provided by genetic change there would be little on which natural selection could operate. Biologists have recognized that in so far as evolution can be explained in positive terms, it is to be seen as arising from the interplay of two factors; one hereditary, the other environmental. Apart from certain *lacunae* a general account of the process can now be given, which traces the history of life from its relatively simple beginning down to the present time. Though certain misunderstandings still abound, theologians for the most part have come

[1] *Quarterly Review*, **108**, 225–264 (1860). Unsigned but generally ascribed to Wilberforce.

to recognize evolution as a valid account from the scientific point of view of a temporal creative process.

Yet it must be admitted that the word 'evolution' is somewhat ill-chosen. It does not accurately describe the process as biology understands it. The word has secular and philosophical overtones, which can be traced back to its early uncritical employment. And it tends to obscure the possibility of theistic interpretation, which as creative process evolution demands. Signifying literally an 'unrolling' or 'unfolding', the word seems to suggest that the final product of the process is somehow contained within its beginning. The implication that the evolutionary process is the unrolling in time of a sequence of living forms, already predetermined in a physical or materialist sense, is neither easily acceptable to theology nor true to the actual teaching of biology. Evolution strictly speaking does not explain the present forms of life in terms of the past: rather it traces the emergence of later forms from earlier. While the environmental factor can perhaps be said to operate as a phenomenal cause with a logic of its own, the hereditary factor is characterized essentially as the occurrence of unpredictable novelty. It is this element which renders the word 'evolution' somewhat inappropriate; since, accepting the theory at its face value, we may say that apart from the occurrence of novelty there would be no evolution.

While much still remains uncertain regarding the actual emergence of new species, the interest of scientists as a whole has currently shifted from the five-hundred-million years or so of the recognizable organic evolutionary process to the even earlier period in which life itself originated. Such evidence as there is for this event comes from somewhat unexpected quarters; and at the present stage of investigation everything is highly speculative. Nevertheless it is possible to discern a feasible process of molecular development, or natural synthesis, by which evolution may be traced back into the realms of biochemistry. A naturally occurring transition from the most highly organized of chemical structures to the most primitive forms recognizable as organic life completes the main lines of the picture from the scientific point of view. It is too early to pronounce definitely on these investigations. What is already significant, however, is that the emphasis on novelty at that point in the process which can be labelled 'the origin of life' ensures in advance that theological interpretation will always have something on which to get a grip. For although the essence of creation is the relation of metaphysical dependence on a Creator, it is invariably the points at which unpredictable novelty occurs that highlight the creative process and call specifically for theological interpretation. So far then from a barren antithesis between the scientific account of origins and the theological doctrine of creation, we can look forward to a progressive collaboration; leading finally to a synthesis of fact and interpretation at a deeper level of understanding than was ever possible in pre-scientific days.

In what follows, I shall attempt a brief sketch of the entire field; though manifestly it will be impossible to review at all adequately the impressive weight of evidence on which the evolutionary view of origins is based. The general remarks which I made in the previous chapter regarding the impossibility of direct experimental verification apply in this field of investigation with the same force as in cosmology. Again the most we can do is to accept as a working hypothesis that account of origins, consistent with experimentally established laws of nature, which accounts for the greatest number of observed facts with the minimum of *ad hoc* supposition. If absolute certainty is not attainable, yet the considered reconstruction of the past has a general reliability which commends it to all open-minded students. Men have been hanged on less evidence. Only when we have surveyed the whole field can we properly engage in theological interpretation.

THE EARTH AND ITS INHABITANTS

The permanence of the terrestrial landscape within the narrow limits of human memory obscures from view the enormous changes which have taken place in the earth's crust during the long period of geological time. Yet some of these changes are manifest even during the course of human history. The weathering of rocks and the consequent sedimentation in coastal regions, volcanic activity, even the rise or fall of land masses, have produced significant alterations during historical time. Geology makes the basic assumption that the present state of the earth's crust is explicable in terms of such processes as these, continuing over immense periods of time. The picture presented by classical geology has been supplemented more recently by geophysical studies, which have enabled us to describe even the inaccessible region inside the earth with some approach to certainty. We know that the solid crust varies in thickness from some seven to fifteen miles, being least under the oceans. Below this lies the mantle, partially fluid, on which the continents float, so to speak, in isostatic equilibrium. At the centre is a core of significantly greater density than the average for the whole earth, believed to be composed largely of molten iron. These are no Jules Verne speculations. Though no man has descended more than a mile or so into the earth's crust, and boring operations can hardly expect ever to sample anything deeper than the surface of the mantle, there are thoroughly reliable techniques capable of telling us a great deal about the interior of the planet. The continuous recording of seismic waves, interpreted by the knowledge of how such waves are propagated, yields direct information about variations in the internal density. Such data, together with a study of gravitational and magnetic anomalies, and of thermal conduction through the crust, enable us to build up a reliable theory of the earth's interior.

But how did the earth come to have this particular structure? On this question scientific opinion has been divided. The earlier view that the earth started as a liquid globe is becoming less and less acceptable. It is considered much more probable that this planet originated as an aggregate of solid particles. Such an aggregate would have to comprise all the chemical elements known to occur on the earth, including those which are radioactive, such as uranium and thorium. As the mass accumulated, the interior would become heated through the liberation of energy from radioactive decay, and melting would proceed from the centre outwards. Two results would be expected to follow: a radial contraction,[1] leading to a buckling of the crust; and convection processes, leading to the rise of the lighter and the fall of the heavier materials. In this way it is possible to account in general terms for the core, the mantle, and the formation of the principle features of the crust. More-

[1] R. A. Lyttleton, *Nature*, **197**, 276 (1963).

over the known rate of radioactive decay enables us to make an estimate of the possible age of the earth, leading to a figure around four-thousand-million years for the establishment of the conditions with which we are familiar.

Classical geology, concerned with the more recent stages of this development, succeeded in arranging the surface rocks in temporal sequence of formation. A system of relative dating, worked out without undue difficulty from an adequate geological survey, shows the younger strata to be rich in fossil forms, recognizably the remains of former living creatures; and these of course provide the basic evidence of the evolutionary process. Absolute dating has become a possibility only since the application of nuclear physics to geological problems. Can we be sure that the law of radioactive decay has remained unchanged throughout geological periods of time? Obviously no direct check is possible. Suffice it to say that converging lines of evidence from the decay of different chemical elements are in substantial agreement.[1] Though of course the absolute ages of rocks quoted in the literature are liable to some degree of error, on the whole they can be accepted as generally trustworthy. Absolute dating by radioactivity, though not applicable to all rocks, gives 'fixes' by which the relative dating of classical geology becomes expressible in quantitative terms. Rocks dated at three-thousand-million years have been identified in Finland, Canada, and South Africa. Ages greater than one-thousand-million years are common in all continents. The Cambrian rocks, the earliest containing appreciable fossil remains, can be dated between five-hundred and six-hundred million years ago. Clearly a detailed scheme of evolution is possible only for the post-Cambrian period, in which fossils are abundant. It is presumably no accident however, that the evolutionary record begins somewhat abruptly in the Cambrian; for manifestly living forms having no skeleton or outer shell will normally not become fossilized. In the nature of the case the most primitive creatures are least likely to leave recognizable traces; and in the exceedingly important pre-Cambrian period evidence tends to be both scanty and somewhat indirect. Yet

---

[1] The remarkable sharpness of pleochroic haloes in certain crystalline ores is also regarded as a valid confirmation of the constancy of radioactive decay.

it is to this period that science must look for any true origin of life.[1]

The fact that science is able to offer a feasible explanation of the origin of life is due in large measure to the new approach to the problem from biochemistry. Living matter is composed principally of a limited group of chemical elements: carbon, hydrogen, oxygen, and nitrogen; with only traces of other elements. On the other hand, though the building units comprise only this narrow range of atoms, the molecules characteristic of living matter are relatively large; containing sometimes hundreds or even thousands of atoms, built up into a complex spatial structure. The essential difficulty faced by any theory of a natural origin of life is to account for the formation of such complex molecules by any random synthetic process. However, direct experiment in the laboratory has shown that random synthesis of fairly complex molecules of these elements takes place slowly under the influence of intense ultra-violet light of extremely short wave-length. Now our present atmosphere contains free oxygen, which in the upper layers is associated as ozone. The extreme ultra-violet received from the sun is strongly absorbed in the ozone layer, and does not penetrate to ground level. The key to the solution of the problem seems therefore to be a radical change in the atmosphere at some time in the remote past. It is now widely believed that the early atmosphere contained no free oxygen, and consequently no ozone. If this was so, then inorganic photo-synthesis would have been a possibility. Colloidal concentration and further synthesis are postulated as the next stage; and proto-life might have originated under such conditions: that is to say, a form of life somewhat akin to those anaerobic organisms still extant; which, unlike higher forms, do not depend upon free oxygen for their metabolism.

Conceivably mutation could have led to plant life of a simple kind; and plant life, as is well known, draws on the carbon dioxide of the atmosphere, from which it generates free oxygen. Indeed it is suggested that the oxygen of the present atmosphere may have been produced entirely by plant life at an early stage

[1] A useful and eminently readable summary of the methods and conclusions of modern geology is available in, M. G. Rutten, *The Geological Aspects of the Origin of Life on Earth.*

in the evolutionary process. These strange speculations are supported by a number of observations whose interpretation is of a somewhat tentative character: for instance by geological studies of certain very ancient sands, the composition of which suggests weathering in an anoxygenic atmosphere. Again traces have been discovered of simple lime-secreting organisms (possibly 2,700 million years old) similar to modern algae, and probably dependent upon an anoxygenic metabolism. Other finds of primitive plant fossils, certainly pre-Cambrian in origin, point to the establishment of a normal atmosphere by perhaps one-thousand-million years ago. Informed opinion is inclined to place the transition from a primitive to a normal atmosphere as a gradual change over the previous thousand-million years. Clearly much more evidence is necessary before these tentative theories can be regarded as well grounded. Even at this stage however, it is right that we should reckon with the possibility of a natural origin of life, and a slow transition from complex but non-living matter to primitive living forms of somewhat greater complexity.[1]

Turning now from the twilight period to post-Cambrian times, a sharp distinction should be noted between the fact of evolution and the theory of evolution. The evidence that the manifold forms of life, past and present, constitute a single kingdom of interrelated organisms is so complete that the fact of evolution can hardly be denied. That every species has come into existence coincident in time and place with closely allied pre-existing species, as Wallace asserted a hundred years ago, is plainly apparent from a study of the rocks and the fossils which they contain. Add to this the structural, chemical, and biological similarities, and substantially the same metabolism among the higher species; and the case for evolution as a fact of natural history becomes unanswerable. The theory of evolution on the other hand is the account of the several mechanisms and causes which are currently held to be responsible for evolutionary progress. Here indeed uncertainties exist at a number of points: there is sometimes room for more than a single view.

---

[1] See again, M. G. Rutten, *loc. cit.;* together with a criticism of some of this author's geological identifications, *Nature*, **197**, 893 (1963). The standard work on the biochemical approach to the problem is, A. I. Oparin, *The Chemical Origin of Life*, trans. A. Synge.

It is obviously important, in embarking on a project of theological interpretation, that we should distinguish clearly between fact and theory. Evolution has happened: exactly how is only partly known.

Moreover the main lines of the evolutionary process are known with some certainty. The divergence of the animal and vegetable kingdoms, and indeed the separation of the principal phylae, had taken place already before the Cambrian era. From this epoch onwards interest naturally focuses on the vertebrates, though it is worth remembering that only a small fraction of living matter is comprised in vertebrate forms. (Microbial life makes up three-quarters of all living matter by sheer weight.) Vertebrate life seems to have originated in the waters: thereafter increasing specialization led successively to amphibians, birds, and mammals. The primates have been on the scene for perhaps twenty million years: man for probably less than one million. Even though the line of descent cannot be traced with certainty at every stage, it is indisputable that the human race is descended, at least bodily, from an animal ancestry.[1] It was inevitable that mankind should have found these facts anything but flattering when first they came to light. There seemed to be nothing left to sustain the traditional conception of the uniqueness of the human creation. Again however, we should make a distinction: between human self-importance, and the status which we believe man to have been given as a child of God. If the facts of evolution do little to sustain the one, they can do nothing to undermine the other. And if evolution seems scarcely credible to the reader who is somewhat unfamiliar with the facts of biology, it is well to remember the enormous number of generations involved in the period of time during which the process has continued. Even the last million years, the possible extent in time of the human race, represents at least forty thousand generations. Contrast this with the few hundred generations of recorded history, and the evolutionary picture is seen in better proportion.

In thinking of the mechanisms and causes which have led to these enormous changes, it is well to adhere to present-day biological opinions. The hereditary factor, mutation, is the apparently spontaneous occurrence of occasional but marked

[1] For an up-to-date treatment see, W. E. Le Gros Clark, *The Antecedents of Man*.

H

differences between an individual and its forbears. Such genetic change can be studied experimentally in those species which multiply with great rapidity: bacilli, drosophila, gammarus etc. If this looks like an artificial simplification of the problem, nevertheless such studies disclose principles which prove useful in a wider context. Genetic change is identified with molecular re-arrangement in the chromosomes of the living cell; and is attributable partly to the effects of natural radiation, partly to other random processes. Genetic change is inheritable: sometimes conferring a marked advantage on an organism, more frequently not. Here is the raw material of evolutionary change according to the generally accepted view.

The environmental factor, natural selection, is grossly misunderstood when it is stigmatized as the 'survival of the fittest'. This empty phrase, which does not need a Darwin for its discovery, has unfortunate overtones and is often a travesty of the facts. Selection proceeds not only through the unavoidable competitive element within a population, but also through mating, natural adaptability, and other factors. What Darwin claimed is that natural selection inevitably leads to the improvement of the majority of organisms in relation to their condition of life.[1] Disadvantageous mutations tend not to be perpetuated; whereas modifications which confer a real advantage in a particular environment are reproduced in increasing proportions. Natural selection is a tendency in nature to pick out and develop those changes which are advantageous in the environment: it operates with a recognizable logic, and is automatically progressive (in Darwin's sense of the word) under the given circumstances.

It is true that some naturalists, Bergson for instance among philosophically-minded biologists, and Raven among theologians, have demanded some teleological factor over and above mutation and selection to account for the progressive movement of evolutionary change. Maybe they are right; though they are swimming against the current. Biological orthodoxy ascribes all evolutionary change to the interplay of the two known factors. The mention of orthodoxy is a reminder that for most practising biologists the theory of evolution has almost the status of a faith. *Lacunae* are admitted; yet new discoveries

See, Julian Huxley, *Nature*, **194**, 44 (1962).

constantly close old gaps, so strengthening the faith of the many. While only time can show the adequacy of the accepted view, it would be folly to base theological interpretation on anything but biological orthodoxy. Only so shall we avoid unnecessary tension and misunderstanding between practising scientists and Christian theologians. Though the material reviewed comprehensively in this section is by no means all of the same degree of probability, the non-scientific reader can rest assured that these are no idle speculations intended to bolster up a materialist philosophy, but informed theories based upon what is known. If they have been allowed too frequently to minister to the materialist outlook, the fault lies more in the lethargy and conservatism of Christians themselves; who have been less forward than they should in claiming the evolutionary process as a whole as the means through which divine creation proceeds from the simplest beginnings to the most highly developed of living creatures, man himself.

CREATIVE PROCESS IN TIME

The detailed interpretation of evolution in theistic terms is a task of some delicacy. It is by no means accomplished by the simple expedient of asserting that the whole process, from biochemistry to man, has been subject to divine guidance. For consider what this would mean. Divine guidance implies a kind of step-by-step prosecution of an overall plan, leading through intended stages to a designed end. Such interpretation does less than justice to the real element of 'trial and error' which the evidence discloses. Moreover it allows us to picture the emergence of man as the 'be all and the end all' of evolutionary change; so denying to the rest of the organic order any value except that of a human ladder. And carried to its logical conclusion such an interpretation is driven to take an unmoral attitude towards the sufferings and pains of lower species, holding that the end justifies the means. In other words, the simple assertion of divine guidance in evolution may turn out to be a denial of the divine goodness: a damning objection from the theological side. From the scientific side too, such interpretation is totally inadequate, since it disguises the randomness of basic natural processes, photo-synthesis and genetic variation;

as it virtually denies the inherent logic of natural selection. I believe the fundamental error of this too facile view of divine guidance lies in a readiness to accept the fact of evolution, while still implicitly rejecting the theory as unduly mechanistic. If we are to succeed, we must interpret the theory of evolution as well as the fact; and this implies whole-hearted acceptance of the theory as practising scientists understand it.

Still more disastrous is it to argue for divine guidance at certain critical turning points in the evolutionary process, on the presumed ground that science is unable to offer an adequate explanation in its own categories. For instance, there is a recognized difficulty in explaining the origin of specific organs (the eye, for example); since it appears that a number of successive mutations would be required, none of which by itself would confer any real advantage on the individual, though an obvious advantage would be conferred by the completed series.[1] There is a strong temptation to suggest that only guidance can ensure that the whole succession of mutations is completed. This is to be resisted, for two reasons. First, because further scientific investigation may well result in a natural explanation being found, so squeezing God out of the gap where we have tried mistakenly to fit him in. Second, because even the most fortuitous occurrence of the right sequence of mutations can by no means be ruled out, somewhere and at some time in the millions of years that are available.

Yet having said this, we recognize that the theological interpretation of evolutionary process involves the relation of natural change to divine control at some level. Otherwise we should be driven to concede that the process is independent of the Creator; that a part of creation has got out of hand, and the final emergence of man is only the result of a remarkable succession of accidents. If we are to avoid the numerous pitfalls, clearly the divine control of nature must be brought in at the ground level, not at the third floor. The evolutionary process, from biochemistry to man, shows us the absolutely logical working out of the laws of nature, on a scale which allows sufficient time to the element of randomness to do its work.

---

[1] This point is discussed in, C. E. Raven, *Experience and Interpretation*, 137–9; and by J. B. S. Haldane, *Nature*, **183**, 713 (1959). See also, D. Lack, *Evolutionary Theory and Christian Belief*, chapters 5 and 6.

Those laws are what they are because nature is God's creation. Atoms, electrons, molecules, light quanta, have the properties and potential possibilities inherent in their createdness. Theism, if it is to succeed, must trace the whole of what happens in nature to the fundamental structure and logic which God has imposed on his creation. If we allow ourselves to see the process of evolution in its totality as following logically and naturally in time from the fundamental structure and behaviour of matter and energy, as they are in themselves, then we have related evolutionary process to the overall divine control. This means that we must make a radical re-appraisal of randomness, and of the logical directedness of natural selection; so that they are recognizably the means used by God in the attainment of his purpose. That these two factors result respectively in the emergence and in the establishment of novelty is sufficient indication that they are creative in the broader sense. They are to be regarded consequently as the instruments of divine creative purpose, seen in its wholeness.

Randomness is not something irrational: chance is not a bogy to be feared. We employ the concepts of chance, randomness, probability, as an intellectual stratagem which enables us to deal with what is unpredictable in detail. The unpredictable is not necessarily without a phenomenal cause: but where the causal relation is exceedingly complex, our minds are unable to cope with the problem of explanation in detail, or to make detailed predictions from prior knowledge of causes. We fall back accordingly on statistical concepts—whether in playing card games, or in studying genetic change. Consequently in recognizing the part played by natural photo-synthesis in the origin of life, or by mutation in the evolution of living forms, we admit to ourselves that here is something unpredictable but not irrational: something moreover in full accord with the kind of order imposed upon nature by its Creator. We may feel some initial surprise that God should use such processes, which we can describe only in terms of randomness, in achieving his creative purpose. But life is full of surprises. If the evidence is sound, as I believe it is broadly, our best course is to accept the fact that God appears to work in this manner. Our understanding may even deepen to the point where this seems to be the only way open to him, if he is not to interfere with the working of nature (inanimate as well as animate) as he has already created it. This is what I mean by a radical re-appraisal of the element of randomness in the evolutionary process.

The creation of novelty by random genetic change involves inevitably the occurrence of numerous mutations disadvantageous to the individual, and indeed to the race, in relation to the conditions under which life is lived. But their very disadvantage, the handicap which they confer, leads logically to their non-establishment under the actual conditions of living. Whereas, on the whole, the advantage conferred by other relatively rare mutations leads by the same logic to their establishment under the same environmental conditions. This is not nature out-of-hand, but nature doing its proper job: natural selection both improving species, and perpetuating improvements already achieved. When we read in Genesis that God saw what he had made and it was good, we understand that every creature was properly suited to the purpose for which it was created. It is not difficult to think of natural selection as the scientific characterization of the process by which this proper adaptation of form to purpose is achieved. And if it seems strange that the Creator should employ methods which we might designate as trial and error, we have to learn that this is but the logical weeding out of the profusion of novelty already implicit in mutation. Reflexion should enable us to see that there is no other way of adapting living forms to environmental conditions, so that they can be said to be 'good'. Of course some degree of suffering exists at all levels of life; and this may present itself as a moral problem to our more sensitive natures: a problem bound up specifically with natural selection. Though we feel the tension keenly, honesty compels us to accept the facts; remembering that suffering is always problematical until it is shared mysteriously by God Incarnate, used and in some sense transformed. In re-appraising the factor of natural selection, we accept this tension; neither minimizing nor exaggerating the significance of suffering below the human level; and finding some degree of insight in a not too literal reading of the eighth chapter of Romans.

To relate the evolutionary process to the divine control of nature in full intellectual honesty, we do not question the two essential mechanisms of genetic change and natural selection as sufficient phenomenal causes. While there can be no tampering with the facts, and no repudiation of orthodox biological theory in the interest of the traditional religious outlook, we are within our rights if we interpret the whole evolutionary process as creative, and see divine guidance principally, or even solely, in the laying down of the fundamental laws of nature. It is sufficient for our purpose to recognize that God exercises an overall control through the reign of law, in the same sense as he exercises control over the phenomena of history through the operation of those principles of personality inherent in the moral ordering of human society. And moreover evolution, like history, has its high-lights, its critical turning-points; where to the eye of faith the divine activity becomes luminous. The origin of life, the emergence of man, are such points. If we are wise, we shall not demand any special guidance here. Rather, the qualitative significance of such turning-points will make us specially aware of the creativity of the whole evolutionary process as ordained by God. But what can we say specifically at these points, which is faithful to our theological insights and also legitimate scientifically?

The origin of life marks a stage of qualitative change, possessing the characteristic of novelty in the fullest degree: novelty unpredictable from within the causal system, but in no way inconsistent with its logical structure. Novelty is the recognizable expression of the creative activity. Hence we shall hold at one and the same time that the origin of organic life is capable of scientific explanation (in principle) in terms of the concepts of biochemistry, and also that it demands interpretation in terms of divine purpose. Scientific explanation, fully valid in its own field, does not exclude theological interpretation; either generally or specifically. Deeper understanding is impossible indeed until we draw on theological categories. And this is the specific Christian contribution: to point to the wonder and mystery, felt even by the dullest; to recognize the qualitatively different potentialities which emerge once a particular level of organization is reached; to draw attention to the novelty as characteristic of personal creative activity. Similarly the emergence of man, from a sub-human ancestry, marks another qualitative step forward, possessing the element of novelty in a supreme degree; and as before novelty spells creation. Again

we can hold that the emergence of man is scientifically explicable (at least so far as his bodily and neural aspects are concerned) and yet in addition demands interpretation in terms of
divine purpose. Each is valid in its own context. Interpretation
illuminates explanation. Here again we recognize a definite
stage in the creative process; the Christian contribution being
to sense the wonder, the potentialities, and the creative novelty,
without denying in any way the full evolutionary account of the
matter.

Further attention should be paid now to the possible limitation imposed on the evolutionary picture of the emergence
of man by the phrase in parentheses, 'at least so far as his
bodily and neural aspects are concerned'. Should we claim
that man, as a self-conscious being capable of fellowship with
his Creator, is fully the product of evolutionary process? Quite
frankly, I do not know. There is of course evidence of mental
process at lower levels of life: evidence of affection, fellowship,
and some sort of understanding among the higher animals, and
between animals and men. Yet we touch that vital distinction
between objective and subjective, external and personal, when
we seek to compare these qualities in animals with what we
take to be their more fully developed counterparts in man. I
know what it is to be a man through the experience of being a
man. I can never know what it is to be a dog. It is not therefore
necessarily obscurantist to believe that the creation of man
involved something more than the final stage of the evolutionary
process, by which (without doubt) man came into being as a
creature with the familiar characteristics of body and brain.
Yet at the same time we have no positive grounds for making
any such assertion. We can repeat all the well-worn arguments
for the infusion of a human soul; but we will refrain. Not one of
them is finally convincing. They do no more than lend support
to one of the possible views. A humble agnosticism has something to commend it here. Let us be content that, by whatever
means, the Creator has endowed man with his mental and
spiritual faculties: that he is fully human. We can let that one
question-mark stand, an admission of our ignorance.

The point we have reached, apart from this one possibility,
is that evolution (biochemical followed by organic) is the
creative process leading to the profusion of living forms and to

man at their peak. It is a strange story, still mysterious even
when explained, covering in all perhaps three-thousand-million
years of slow change. Properly appreciated it provides the
material for a tentative re-writing of Genesis i. Man, as he has
emerged, is one with the whole organic order: as the peak of
creative process, he knows fellowship with his Creator. Process
has blossomed into self-consciousness; and the end is not yet,
for the new creation supervenes upon the old. Basically this is
the vision which inspired de Chardin to write his remarkable
book, *The Phenomenon of Man*. That work indeed presents a view
of the subject which is sometimes more poetic than scientific,
and which is vitiated by some of the loosest use of language that
has ever been offered to the reading public. It leads to a
philosophical conclusion which implicitly blurs the distinction
between the Creator and the goal of the creative process.
Rapturously applauded by the many, devastatingly pulverized
by the few,[1] what has it achieved? My own opinion is that it has
reinstated teleology: no mean accomplishment after a century
of undiluted evolutionism. While its basis is still not permanently
secured in a scientific age, teleology is once more becoming
intellectually respectable.

Ask me for a definition of teleology, and I shall not be content
to quote the dictionaries. Teleology is emerging in the new
situation as *the discernment of purpose in process*. In no sense is it,
nor I think can it ever become, a scientific category. It is
supra-scientific: something which must be added to any
scientific explanation, however complete, if we are to do justice
to the sense of wonder and mystery inspired by the contempla-
tion of the created order. For long years out of fashion in a
predominantly scientific culture, it has been kept alive by
theologians—on drip-feed and blood-transfusion. Now it is
convalescent. Soon it will come into its own again in a richer
form; and men will wonder how they got along without it. For
teleology is the ultimate intellectual act of faith of the man who
knows the facts and accepts the theories of science, and refuses
to shut his eyes to either.

In sum, what is the position? Evolution is the organic
creative process; and it is essentially temporal. Organic creation
takes place not by the divine *fiat*, as by a wellnigh instantaneous

[1] P. B. Medawar, for instance, in *Mind*, **70**, 99–106 (1961).

act of will; but through the gradual accumulation of infinitesimal changes in that which exists already, so bringing into being in the course of many generations that which is qualitatively different. Recognizing the divine undergirding of nature at the fundamental level, we can accept the logic of the process itself, the relative autonomy of the organic world, and the 'inevitability of gradualness'. If with Bergson we can speak of 'creative evolution', it is because we discern an order, divinely imposed upon matter and energy in temporal relation, such that organic life in all its diversity emerges as the logical working out of what was from the beginning an inherent possibility. As Christians we claim that evolution is not meaningless. We insist on the right to interpret process in terms of the relation between Creator and creature, Self-existent and contingent, Dramatist and drama; recognizing novelty as the hall-mark of creative activity, and the relative autonomy of living creatures not as an indication that the process is out of control but as a measure of the dramatic power of the Master Dramatist. To pursue the matter further we need the category of eternity; and this must be left until we have elucidated the relationship of the eternal to the temporal.

VIII

THE RELATIVITY OF TIME

FOR normal purposes both the plain man and the scientist are apt to assume that distances and times can be observed by the correct use of measuring rod or clock as the case may be. Neither of these procedures, however, is quite as straightforward as at first appears: yet observations of distance and time are basic to any exact science. It is axiomatic that knowledge of the external world is logically dependent upon our ability to make and to interpret valid observations. Anything which purports to be an item of natural knowledge is meaningful only if we can specify, at least in principle, how such information is to be obtained by appropriate valid observational procedures. We have already encountered the problem of spatial and temporal measurement on the astronomical scale, the field in which epistemological questions are most urgent; and we are aware that the interpretation of all such observations is beset by serious conceptual difficulties, with consequential limitation of our possible knowledge of external reality on the grand scale. The resolution of these and kindred problems brings together the long-separated disciplines of philosophy and mathematical physics; the theory of relativity (in its special and general forms) being the outcome. What this means in practice is that the foundations of a comprehensive natural philosophy have been laid afresh by Einstein in the early years of the present century, on a more searching analysis than was possible in the classical age of Newton.

In what follows we shall concern ourselves only with certain very general principles; leaving aside all mathematical development, apart from the mere statement of a few formulae. The problem of the interpretation of astronomical observations provides a suitable starting point, though the principles which will emerge are of far wider generality. Our view of the heavens, we said earlier,[1] does not show us the present positions and states of the various astronomical objects, because the velocity of light is finite. What does this really mean? What precise conceptual limitation does it impose upon our knowledge of the universe? Since our enquiry must start from first principles, we must assume for the present that the velocity of light is unknown. It cannot be known until validly determined; and its experimental determination is beset by the very difficulties, attendant on spatial and temporal observation, to which we are now giving attention. The distances of the various astronomical objects also must be regarded as unknown at this stage of the discussion. Clearly these two uncertainties are closely linked.

Although the first indication that light travels with a finite velocity was provided by astronomical observation, any accurate measurement of the velocity demands a terrestrial experiment. The earth however is a moving platform: a fact which introduces its own conceptual complications. Suffice it to say for the present that preliminary work suggests that error on this account will be exceedingly small. The determination of the velocity of light under terrestrial conditions involves the precise measurement of the extremely short interval of time taken by light to travel over a measured distance. But how is the observer to know when the light signal, which he sends out, arrives at the other end of the measured distance? He can only be in one place at once. He can know the time of arrival of his own light signal (a distant event) only by means of a return light signal sent back along the same path. Here we see the essence of the problem: it is impossible for us to have strictly instantaneous knowledge of an event at a distance. Or to put it another way, we have no self-evident procedure by which we can establish the simultaneity of two events occurring at widely separated points.

As regards the determination of astronomical distances, the basic technique of the surveyor is serviceable in the case of the nearer heavenly bodies. The distance of the sun, and therefore the dimensions of the earth's orbit, is readily determined from a sufficiently long terrestrial base-line. The diameter of the earth's orbit then provides a base-line for the determination of

[1] See Chapter VI.

the distance of the nearest stars. But notice this. All these calculations assume the validity of Euclidean geometry over great distances of space. It is true of course that the propositions of Euclid rest on rigorous proof. The proofs however rest on the axioms; which are held to be self-evident, because they represent adequately our immediate geometrical apprehensions of the limited space in which we live. What right have we to suppose these axioms universally valid?[1] Different axioms result in different geometries, such as are employed for instance in general relativity. It is sufficient for our purpose, however, to observe that our normal geometry is not self-evidently applicable to astronomical distances: another example of the fundamental conceptual difficulties under which an exact science labours.

Here then are the elements of our problem: the meaning of simultaneity, and the interpretation of the observations of what we call distance. A natural philosophy is properly based epistemologically only when these matters have been attended to. And it is the former which concerns us here more particularly.

THE PROBLEM OF SIMULTANEITY

In order to understand the conceptual situation we begin by defining a specific observational problem. We ask then what observations are physically possible. Finally we enquire what meaning is to be attached to these observations, what knowledge they afford us.

First the problem. Imagine two points P and Q in space, so far apart from one another that a direct measurement of the distance PQ with a measuring rod is quite impracticable. We assume also that P and Q do not move relatively to one another: how this is to be arranged in practice is irrelevant. Suppose now that I am situated at P; while at Q there is another observer with whom I can communicate by light-signalling (or radio), and whom I can persuade to co-operate in the experiment. Apart from such signalling there is no contact between us.

Now the kind of observation that is physically possible. We are concerned with velocities, times, and distances. But the conditions of the problem are such that I cannot measure

---

[1] P. W. Bridgman, *The Logic of Modern Physics*, 14–18, 67.

distance in the accustomed manner. Clearly the only instrument that I can employ is a clock; and I am entitled to assume that my clock gives me a temporal series of equally-spaced ticks; each of which corresponds to a perceptible movement of the hands, so saving the necessity of counting ticks. I can also send out a light-signal at any instant I choose by flashing a lamp. The other observer, situated at Q, agrees to send back a return light-signal at the precise moment when he receives my signal. I can then read off on my clock the time interval between sending out my signal and receiving his.

Finally, the interpretation of the observations. I send out a light-signal when my clock reads a time t_1. I receive the return signal when it reads t_2. Clearly, the difference $(t_2 - t_1)$ represents the time taken by my light-signal to travel from P to Q, plus the time taken by the return signal to travel from Q to P, since I assume that the other observer loses no time in flashing his lamp. But what does this tell me about the instant at which he received my signal? Nothing very precise. The only observational evidence I have that he received my signal is the arrival of his return signal. No information can be transmitted from Q to P faster than light. It may even be meaningless for me to talk about the instant of time at which the distant observer received my signal, for I cannot know it by direct observation. All I know is the two times t_1 and t_2, the instants at which I sent and received light-signals. And I infer that the distant observer received my signal at some instant which on my clock must be intermediate between t_1 and t_2. Yet I want some procedure, or convention, by which I can define simultaneity, so giving meaning to the concept. That is to say, I want to know how to fix a point on my clock at P which corresponds in time to an event at the distant station Q. Einstein's theory lays down the appropriate procedure, which though apparently obvious has the status of a necessary presupposition. The time t, at which the distant observer receives my signal and sends out his return signal, is to be expressed in terms of my clock by the equation,

$$t = t_1 + \tfrac{1}{2}(t_2 - t_1)$$

i.e.
$$t = \tfrac{1}{2}(t_2 + t_1)$$

But it must be realised that this statement contains an element of arbitrariness. Though it looks reasonable enough, it cannot be established rigorously. It is to be regarded as a definition of what is meant by simultaneity: and without such a definition we could proceed no further.

What does this equation imply about light? That between two observers relatively at rest the velocity of light is taken to be the same in either direction. Taking the velocity of light to be c, and the distance from P to Q (in terms of Euclidean geometry) to be r, Einstein's procedure gives

$$r = \tfrac{1}{2}c \,(t_2 - t_1)$$

Of course this relation between velocity and distance and time looks exceedingly obvious: we naturally think of the light-signal as a kind of express train, obeying the same kinematical laws. What we have to recognize is the basic assumption on which the relation rests: the absence of relative motion, and the constancy of the velocity of light. Apart from these assumptions it would not be justified. And having adopted it here, we realize that the problem would be materially different when P and Q are allowed to move relatively to one another.

This simple relation for observers in relative rest enables us to determine the velocity of light by terrestrial experiment. For now let P and Q be two points at a *measured* distance apart *on the earth's surface*. Whatever the motion of the earth in space, clearly the condition of no relative motion is satisfied. We replace the distant observer at Q by a system of lenses and a mirror, designed so as to send the original light-signal back to P; thereby obviating any human delay in the second observer, who is now out of work. A highly sensitive device at P measures the time interval taken by the light for the double journey. In Fizeau's classical experiment, the first terrestrial determination to succeed, the timing device was a revolving toothed wheel; arranged to 'chop up' the outgoing beam of light into a succession of pulses as it passed between the teeth. If on return these pulses of light are just obscured by the next tooth of the wheel, the time interval $(t_2 - t_1)$ is known from the rate of rotation, and c may be calculated. Later and more accurate determinations of the velocity of light use more sensitive timing devices, but the principle is essentially similar.[1]

---

[1] Ultimate precision depends on the timing device. Using modern electrical techniques an accuracy considerably better than one part in a million is attained. The velocity of light *in vacuo* is very nearly 3×10^{10} cm/sec. or 186,000 miles/sec.

Terrestrial experiments such as the foregoing might be expected to yield differing results according to the direction of the line PQ with respect to the motion of the earth. Such differences, if they exist, are well within the range of detection. Yet the most sensitive experiments have failed consistently to show any measurable difference in the velocity of light in different directions on the earth's surface. The Michelson and Morley experiment, which first established this strange result in 1887, though the full implications were not immediately realized, provided the logical justification of the special theory of relativity. Since the motion of the earth in space does not apparently affect the velocity of light relative to a terrestrial observer, Einstein was led to postulate the absolute constancy of this velocity for all observers as a fundamental fact of nature. The strange paradoxes of relativity are the direct consequences of this postulate. Even if some of the deductions of relativity theory appear to be at variance with ordinary common sense, we have to remember that the theory is logically based on exceedingly precise observations, and many of its predictions have been experimentally established. Our common-sense expectations are what they are because in ordinary life we never deal with entities moving at a rate approaching the velocity of light. If we did, our everyday outlook would no doubt be different. It appears however, that the velocities of the more distant astronomical objects relative to ourselves, are sufficiently large for relativity effects to be significant.

To return now to the hypothetical experiment with two observers. The conditions are notably different if we assume that P and Q move relatively to one another. It is implicit in the theory of relativity that we can have no knowledge of any absolute motions of material bodies. In the absence of acceleration, each observer thinks of himself as being at rest and the other observer as in motion. Epistemologically therefore, the two observers are on the same footing. Each is entitled to his own view of the universe; each makes his own observations: but in general we shall not expect precise agreement between them. In order to make the problem precise, we suppose the two observers P and Q to be equipped now with identical clocks. Although they are in relative motion, they may be supposed to pass sufficiently close to one another at some moment for both observers to set their respective clocks to zero at the same instant. Thereafter they continue to separate at a relative velocity v; and to exchange reciprocal light-signals as in the previous experiment. The two sets of observations can be visualized with the help of Figure 1, in which two diverging

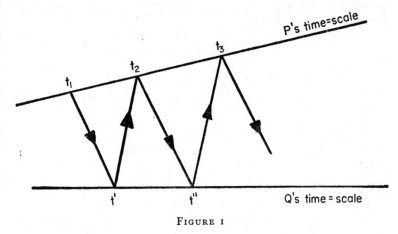

FIGURE I

lines represent the time-scales of the two observers.[1] The exchange of light-signals is indicated by the zigzag lines, and the observed times are as shown. Thus:

t_1 is the time on P's clock when P sends a signal to Q.

t' is the time on Q's clock when Q receives this signal, and sends a return signal to P.

t_2 is the time on P's clock when P receives the return signal, and sends another signal to Q; and so on.

Each observer can see only his own clock. The times t_1, t_2, t_3, etc., are recorded on P's clock, and are unknown to Q. The times t', t'', etc., are recorded on Q's clock, and are unknown to P. Both observers are in the same logical situation. Can we establish any temporal relationship between them, as we did in the simpler case of two observers without relative motion? Specifically, what is the time t on P's clock which corresponds to the arrival of the first signal at Q; the time, that is, which Q records on his own clock as t'?

---

[1] The positions and directions of these two lines in the diagram are entirely arbitrary.

I

In addition to the postulate of the constancy of the velocity of light, the same for both observers, one more fact is known. Because the two observers are in logically equivalent positions, it follows that the time t' stands in the same relation to the time t_1, as the time t_2 stands to the time t'. These are the basic principles. The reader can be spared the calculation[1]; but the final result is interesting:

$$t = t' \,/\, \sqrt{1 - v^2/c^2}$$

Although the conditions imposed on the problem appear somewhat artificial, in reality we have merely stripped away all irrelevant information and false presuppositions from the situation of an actual observer in a moving system, who wishes to obtain valid information about another moving system. The resulting formula expresses the temporal relationship of the two systems. For the times t and t' refer to the same instantaneous event; namely, the reception and return of a signal by a distant observer. This distant event occurs at time t' on the clock which moves with the system Q; but from the point of view of the first observer P, it must be assigned to a quite different time t. The clocks are identical, and have been set to zero at the same moment; yet the concept of simultaneity has lost all meaning. The formula shows moreover that t is always greater than t'. The difference becomes more pronounced the greater the relative velocity of the two systems, and is independent of the direction of this relative motion. Interpreted in words, this means that P, who trusts his own clock, regards Q's clock as losing time. And since the effect is reciprocal, Q similarly regards P's clock as losing time. Judged by the man on the spot, each clock is keeping good time: judged by the distant observer, each clock is running slow. In the limit, as the relative velocity approaches that of light, each observer is under the impression that the distant clock has almost stopped.

This curious phenomenon is known as the 'dilatation of time'. Its implications for our general view of the universe are important. We naturally tend to assume that there is such a thing as universal time; in other words that two observers must necessarily assign the same time to any particular event wherever it

<hr/>

[1] See G. J. Whitrow, *The Natural Philosophy of Time*, 200–209.

occurs. But this is not so in a universe in which there is relative motion. This result may be expressed figuratively as a matter of perspective. We are familiar with differences of spatial perspective: objects appear in different relative positions according to the position of the observer. Now we must recognize also a difference of temporal perspective: events appear to occur at different relative times according to the motion of the observer.

Possibly the most striking feature of the relativity of time is the so-called 'clock paradox'; though unfortunately there is not complete agreement among the experts as to the validity of this extension of the argument. Let us suppose however that the observer Q is sent off for a long voyage in a space-ship, cruising at a relative velocity which approaches that of light. From the point of view of P, who remains on earth, Q's clock is slowed down enormously; and it seems reasonable to suggest that his metabolic processes are similarly slowed down from the point of view of the earth-bound P. After some years, Q makes the return trip to earth, moving still with the high relative velocity. He arrives, still in the prime of his age, to find his fellow observer P an old man. There's nothing like a space-trip to keep you young! Is the argument valid? Are these temporal changes real or apparent? What are the effects of the enormous deceleration and acceleration, involved in reversing the motion of the space-ship? More disarming still, what has happened to the postulate of reciprocity? Discussion continues; and unfortunately (or fortunately) the rocket engineers are nowhere near being able to put it to the test. Rejuvenation by space travel remains a pipe-dream.

The result of real significance is the dilatation of time, the difference of temporal perspective arising from relative motion. This is fully agreed by the experts.[1] Time is relative to the observer. We can no longer think in terms of a universal or cosmic time, valid for the entire universe. There is no such thing as universal simultaneity. Any judgement that two events occur at the same time is dependent on the motion of the observer; and in general different observers judge differently. Thus, the position of an observer in space, his situation in time, and his velocity, can be known only relatively. Absolute knowledge of

[1] There is even experimental confirmation from the observed life-times of μ-mesons liberated in the upper atmosphere by cosmic rays.

any one of these quantities is impossible in principle; and hence the concepts themselves, recognized now as observationally meaningless, must disappear from any comprehensive natural philosophy whose logical foundations are secure. The normal laws of mechanics and electro-magnetism, etc., still have validity within what is known as an 'inertial system'.[1] But in the most general problems of cosmology, space, time, and velocity, must be represented as relative to the inertial system within which the observer is situated; and the possibility of absolute knowledge of anything except the velocity of light *in vacuo* must be rigorously excluded. If 'relativity' is a term of opprobrium in philosophical theology, it is none the less fundamental to accurate thinking about the phenomena of nature. That time is relative to the individual is a particular conclusion of our analysis, which must have far-reaching implications for any valid philosophical-theological characterization of the universe as it is apprehended by human minds.

SPACE-TIME REPRESENTATION

The problem which arises now is the conceptual representation of external reality in terms of space and time. Since our possible knowledge of both these parameters is relative to the observer, the idea of perspective being applicable equally in either case, we must devise a comprehensive system of representation which takes account fully of the present conceptual situation. We can proceed by analogy; adding a temporal dimension to the three recognized spatial dimensions. The result is the space-time continuum of relativity theory.

Any observer, a scientist working on earth for instance, viewing the whole array of external events, is entitled to assign to each an observed position and an observed time relative to himself. The usual representation of space makes use of three rectangular co-ordinates, the position of a point P being defined by the lengths of the three perpendiculars drawn to the three planes which meet at the origin.[2] In Figure 2, three mutually

---

[1] A. Einstein and L. Infeld, *The Evolution of Physics*. For definition of such systems, see p. 158. For the existence of such systems see pp. 209–212.

[2] For instance, regard one corner of the floor of the room as origin of co-ordinates, and the three edges which meet in this corner as axes.

perpendicular axes are represented by OX, OY, OZ; and the co-ordinates which specify the position of a point P are represented . . .

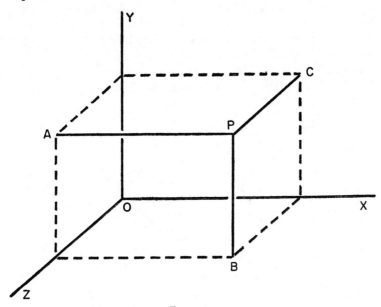

FIGURE 2

by $x = PA$, $y = PB$, $z = PC$. Three mutually perpendicular dimensions represent fully the spatial perspective, the point P being designated (x, y, z). Now we are required to think not just of a point in a three-dimensional space, but of a point-event in space and time. If we observe correctly a moving particle, we make a temporal as well as a spatial observation. The observed position (x, y, z) corresponds to an observed time t on our clock. The question is, how to extend our representation to include the temporal observation with the spatial in a single system. For this purpose we require a fourth co-ordinate; but this additional dimension must be reduced to the same scale as the original three if it is to be satisfactorily combined with them in a single representational system. This can be done by converting the time co-ordinate into a space-like co-ordinate, using the velocity of light as a conversion factor. All events can then be represented in a four-dimensional continuum, which is described as space-time. It is neither space, nor is it time; but a subtle combination of the two separate perspectives of the one observer. And of course it is not possible to draw a single diagram which properly indicates all four dimensions together. The most we can do on a single diagram is to represent any three of the four dimensions of space-time: for normal purposes however, the most useful diagram is one which shows the time axis and one only of the space axes on the plane of the paper. Such a representation is known as a 'Minkowski diagram'.

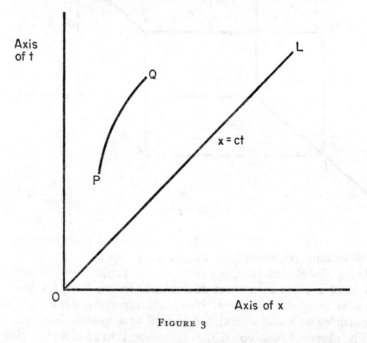

FIGURE 3

Figure 3 shows such a two-dimensional diagram, drawn so as to represent time, and extension in the *x* direction. Neither of the other spatial co-ordinates is shown. A Minkowski diagram therefore gives merely a convenient sample of the full information contained in the undrawable four-dimensional continuum. But in a simplified manner it enables us to grasp the concept of space-time. Any point on the diagram can now signify an event occurring at a particular position in the spatial co-ordinate system of the observer, and at a particular time in his temporal experience. Such a point is referred to as a point-instant, or more usually as a *world-point*. The continuous line *PQ* therefore represents the continuing existence of a material particle in motion relative to the observer; since every point on the line represents a particular observed position of the particle and the corresponding time observation. The line *PQ*, which may be straight or curved depending on the motion of the particle, is the *world-line* of the particle. The line *OL* is the world-line of a ray of light travelling parallel to the observer's axis of *x*. Since its velocity is *c*, it is represented by the equation $x = ct$, and accordingly is shown as making equal angles with the two axes. The world-lines of all material particles must lie between *OL* and the axis of *t*, since their velocities cannot exceed *c*.

Clearly the four-dimensional continuum, of which a Minkowski diagram is a sample only, can represent adequately the whole of external physical reality as observed and known by a particular observer. Every particle of matter and every ray of light is represented by its own appropriately drawn world-line: the external world by the totality of all conceivable world-lines. True, the space-time of one observer differs from that of another who moves relatively to him. But the relativity of our knowledge of external reality is correctly safeguarded by this manner of representation; and all the laws of nature known to us are valid within such a representational framework. For purely scientific purposes this is all that can be desired.

The wider philosophical implications of the 'discovery' of space-time are not entirely clear however: it is important that we give some attention to this question. We want to ask what is the status of the space-time continuum. Is it merely a convenient mental construct? a representational device which enables us to handle our observations coherently? Or does it give a privileged view of reality? Such that we must say, The external world is like this, and any attempt to conceive it otherwise involves serious epistemological error. And if external reality *must* be conceived in this way, how is our immediate apprehension of distance and time (as distinct from the techniques employed in their measurement) related to the space-time of Einstein's theory?

I say we *want* to ask these questions: but have we any right to do so? I strongly suspect that they are meaningless; for we can know nothing of the external world, and the nature of its reality, except by making observations as precise as possible, and interpreting them with a full realization of the limits of their validity. It is surely axiomatic that reality cannot be known as it is in itself. The most we can accomplish is a conceptual system, with its appropriate rules, which is not inconsistent with observation, and which permits us to predict further relations capable of observational test. In the past it was held without question that spatial extension and temporal duration are separate and independent observable characters of external reality. Such was the epistemological basis of Newton's physics; but it proved to be an inadequate representation of physical reality. 'Instead of asserting with Locke that *every* part of space is in *every* part of time and *every* part of time is in *every* part of space, Minkowski (following Einstein) pointed out that "Nobody has ever noticed a place except at a time, or a time except at a place." . . . Minkowski's object was to provide a new substitute for the Newtonian absolute space and absolute time discarded by Einstein. In their place he advocated his absolute "world" which gave different "projections" in space and in time for different observers (associated with inertial frames of reference).'[1] The new point of view therefore asserts strongly the indivisibility of our spatial and temporal knowledge of the external world. 'The scene of action of reality is not a three-dimensional Euclidean space, but rather a *four-dimensional world, in which space and time are linked together indissolubly.* However deep the chasm may be that separates the intuitive nature of space from that of time in our experience, nothing of this qualitative difference enters into the objective world which physics endeavours to crystallize out of direct experience.'[2] In other words, a proper attention to the epistemological basis of our observations compels us to adopt a relativist point of view; and the status of space-time is that of the most perfect representation of external reality available to us, which for purposes of natural philosophy we are entitled to identify with external reality itself; provided we are cognizant of the distinction between 'appearances' and 'things in themselves'.

[1] G. J. Whitrow, *The Natural Philosophy of Time*, 224.
[2] H. Weyl, *Space, Time, Matter* (trans, Brose), 217.

Physically the time-dimension of the four-dimensional continuum is not different in character from the other three. Nor is this surprising when we remember that both distances and times (whatever they are in themselves) are reduced to number before being represented in co-ordinate form. It is these measures, obtained by observational procedures, that are handled in natural philosophy. Consequently any attempted unification in a four-dimensional framework must begin by recognizing spatial and temporal measures as formally equivalent. From this point, however, two courses are open to us: (1) Either, time is to be represented by a space-like dimension; and the resulting continuum, though it is neither space nor time, is spatially conceived. (2) Or, space is to be represented by a time-like dimension; and the resulting continuum is temporally conceived. Whichever course is adopted, the coefficient of equivalence between length and duration is numerically equal to the velocity of light *in vacuo*. It is a fact however, that Minkowski and all who have followed him have chosen to adopt the former alternative. What de Beauregard calls 'the spatialization of time' is the consequence. 'La Physique relativiste peut se définir en un sens par sa volonté déterminée de ne pas prendre le temps comme variable indépendante.'[1] We may not be entitled to ask whether space and time are notions humanly extracted from a really-existing space-time; or whether space-time is merely a mental construct of the two basic subjective apprehensions which we designate space and time respectively. What we do recognize is that it is possible to conceive a number of space-like dimensions mutally at right angles; whereas it is quite impossible to conceive more than one time-like dimension. In view of this limitation, we are surely right to follow Minkowski, unifying our conception of external reality by representation in terms of a space-time continuum which is space-like.

We are then permitted to regard space-time as the true mode of external reality, in so far as it is humanly comprehensible; and to treat space and time equally and in the same sense as subjective experiences of consciousness, derived from our objective existence in space-time. In earlier chapters we have shown reason for regarding time as essentially a subjective

[1] O. Costa de Beauregard, *La Notion de Temps*, 202.

IX

EVERLASTING OR ETERNAL?

WE return now to a problem which was touched on in the first chapter but then laid aside: namely the confusion created by the indiscriminate use of such words as 'eternal' and 'everlasting'. For religious and theological purposes we need some way of marking off the being of God from the finite existence in time which is ours. How is this to be done in a satisfactory manner?

Of course this is not primarily a matter of conforming to long philosophical usage. If it were, 'everlasting' as a characterization of the divine could be dismissed immediately as philosophically naïve, an unwanted remainder from primitive religious insight; and the being of God would be conceived by the light of reason in terms of eternity, in the sense of timelessness. Christian theology, however, is a discipline distinguished sharply both from religion and from philosophy. To be sure, it has affinities in both directions. From biblical religion it draws the insights which are basic to it: Christian theology can never cut itself adrift from the revealed knowledge of God to be found in the first instance in the scriptures. It is essentially an empirical study, with an obligation to remain faithful to a body of empirical evidence. On the other hand it makes an appeal to reason; and this means that its formulation of divine truth must not offend against the canons of consistent thinking. Christianity 'does not profess to proclaim standing truths about God derived either from the *a priori* deliverances of human reason, or from revelation received in the form of ready-made propositions. What it has to proclaim is a gospel, the good news of what God has done and is doing in the history of this world, and its theology, its exposition of standing truths about God, is derived from reflection upon those divine acts. But this reflection is an activity of the reason, and whilst the first duty in accurate thinking is to accept the given material without denying it, distorting it, or explaining it away, and whilst it may be necessary to acknowledge an element of mystery beyond our understanding, the mystery must not be one which is essentially irrational'.[1] This is well said. The factual basis of our theology is something given once for all in what is recognized as divine activity in the past, and ratified contemporarily in the Christian way of life. In constructing a rationally satisfying intellectual system the theologian attempts to answer the question, What must be the nature of the Godhead and the mode of his Being if the facts of our Christian experience are what the Bible declares them to be?

Theology therefore must draw on the philosophical tradition as it has developed historically, just as the patristic writers drew on the Greek tradition. In saying this, we recognize that the philosophical stream has broadened considerably in our own day, as the several scientific tributaries have flowed into it. Specifically, we have a better understanding of temporality through our modern analysis of time-measurement, entropy-change, cosmology, and evolutionary process: all of which is highly relevant to our rational thinking about the being of God. But the humility of mind which is inseparable from Christian insight does not permit the theologian to make the claim of absolute truth for the rational *system* which he develops. Theological thought is analogical through and through. It has temporary validity indeed for the Christian who shares in the experience on which it is based and which it attempts to rationalize. We dare to claim that it is a useful, helpful, legitimate way of thinking about the Ground of our being; which is consistent with the facts of Christian experience, both biblical and contemporary, and with such insights into the nature of reality as modern studies have disclosed. In our present context therefore the question is not the purely philosophical enquiry into the relationship of the divine to the human and temporal. Rather we ask, How can we most usefully and legitimately think of the mode of being of God, consistently with our Christian position and our modern understanding of temporal process?

[1] L. Hodgson, *The Doctrine of the Trinity*, 109.

FROM EVERLASTING TO EVERLASTING

We begin by assuming that any religious statement in biblical language, whether transparent or perplexing, originates in spiritual experience which was shared by a number of people. The knowledge of God contained in scripture, shared as it is among its immediate contemporaries, is exhibited also as a recognizable strand running throughout the thousand years of biblical composition. Development of course there is, as the progressive revelation is received; but development of a character which emphasizes continuity. Consequently, throughout the biblical period of writing the sharedness of man's experience of God may be said to transcend the time of the present moment; in the sense that men who are not contemporaries have, and know one another to have, comparable religious experience. Such is the factual basis of all theological thinking.

The time-span of the Bible's experience of God, together with the apprehension of his constancy, lead naturally (though perhaps not logically) to extrapolation backwards and forwards in history. The character which God has shown towards man in his mighty acts, as far back in time as men have recorded their experience, is taken intuitively to be the character which he has shown towards men since the beginning of the human race, and which he will continue to display as long as the race lasts. In this respect human intuition must be seen as the correlative of divine revelation. God has revealed himself progressively, and in Christ finally, in such a way that the man of religion is fully justified in expressing the character of God as constant from the dawn of history to its close. The attempt to get inside the minds of the men of the Bible, and to apprehend revealed truth in its original form, marks the present goal of the critical movement. And biblical theology, which might be defined as the rationale of the divine self-revelation as originally received, insists on speaking of God in purely temporal terms. Because God was known as active in history, he was historically conceived. Creation, revelation, redemption, and consummation, one and all are referred to the time-series. The Lord of history, if not historically conditioned, is historically located on the widest conceivable canvas. He is 'from everlasting to everlasting'.

Now of course this biblical phrase expresses strictly speaking an exceedingly long but not an infinite period of time. We are commonly informed that the Hebrews did not think of time as we do; but we have seen already how difficult it is to understand precisely how they did think of temporal process.[1] Philosophically their thought was primitive, and in a degree naïve. The problems which bother us today did not apparently occur to them: it is useless therefore to look to them for the answers. Specifically, the concept of infinite time probably never entered their heads. Why should it indeed? Though culturally a simple people, the Hebrews were essentially realists. And if it is the *experience* of the divine that we are discussing, then the total span of human history is the longest period of time that is at all relevant.

Not until the patristic age, when the Greek philosophical tradition began to be integrated with the content of the biblical revelation, did the question of the *being* of God as he is in himself become a live issue. Only then did the concept of a timeless eternity begin to make its contribution to human thinking about the being of the God who is revealed in the history and the scriptures of the Hebrew people: and then, be it noticed, as a medium in which to express the truth rather than as a parallel source of knowledge. In some respects the philosophical legacy of a timeless eternity has been almost as much of an embarrassment as a help. The problem of relating the timelessness of God as he is in himself to the facts of a revelation in time and an 'intervention' in the temporal process are still incompletely resolved. It is for this reason among others that the present generation has inclined towards a biblical theology; but whatever have been the gains in biblical insight, the key problem has been shelved rather than solved by this renewed insistence on the primitive, even naïve, views of time current among the Hebrews.

Unless checked, this enforced separation of religious and philosophical thinking is likely to prove disastrous for the study of theology properly so-called. For the period of history which has witnessed the revival of biblical modes of thought is the same which has been driven by cosmological research to visualize the possibility of infinite time. The relation between

[1] See Chapter II.

scientific thinking about the temporal order and the essential insights of the Christian revelation is being forced upon our attention: it will be lamentable indeed if our generation fails to address itself to this central problem of philosophical theology. To entertain the speculative conclusions of cosmology, while thinking in purely biblical categories on points of theology, is to abandon all rational hold on the doctrine of creation; so inviting scepticism and unbelief. Our vocation today is to discover how the essential biblical insights may be expressed in an intellectually respectable form; consistently, that is, with modern horizons in philosophy and science. In the present-day idiom, this is a 'must'.

Perhaps the first step is to explore the meaning of the phrase, 'from everlasting to everlasting': considering it tentatively in terms of a possibly infinite time-scale; even though the biblical authors were innocent of any such conception. At least we then recognize that what they were saying is that there is no conceivable time at which God is not; no time at which he has not the character revealed historically in the scriptures. However, to conceive the existence of God in the mode of endless time is fraught with difficulties. In saying this, I am not thinking primarily of Kant's well-known antinomies, which have been held to vitiate the conception of infinite time; nor yet of the alleged impossibility that at the present moment an infinite time has already elapsed. This view, inherent not in time itself but in a causal theory of time, has been disposed of satisfactorily (I believe) by C. D. Broad.[1] For purposes of mathematics, the concept of infinite time is commonplace. Though it necessarily transcends our human experience, and consequently our powers of imagination, the concept is not thereby rendered irrational; and indeed it may have its place in our conceptual representation of the physical order. The essential difficulty which we encounter when we try to think of God in terms of an indefinitely extended time-scale is the nature of time itself. The experience of time is the experience of change: subjectively in the first instance, though later for public purposes it is referred to objective change in the external world.

If the temporal order is characterized essentially by the changing of that which exists, then two possibilities only are

[1] C. D. Broad, Art. *Time,* in *E.R.E.*

open to us when we attempt to extend the time-scale to infinity. Either we must think of a process in which change continues indefinitely in a particular direction; and in this case infinite time can correspond only to infinite change. That is to say, the entity which is subject to change changes out of all recognition. Or we must think of some cyclic process, such that the entity repeats a particular series of changes an endless number of times, constantly returning to the same state. In this case the entity remains recognizable indeed, but the infinity is one of repetition: the concept of infinite time reduces to an unlimited numerical progression. The one procedure gives us a possibly infinite time-scale such as might be based on the universe as a whole: the other a scale such as might be based on the movements of the solar system. What is absolutely beyond question is that no scale of time can be rendered meaningful except in terms of physical change of some kind. What we cannot have is an infinitely extended temporal scale without an infinitely extended temporal process of a physical character. In interpreting 'from everlasting to everlasting' in terms of a possibly infinite time-scale, we were trying to say that there is no conceivable time at which God is not. But clearly now this cannot imply that God is temporally located. To locate the deity in the time-series, even if infinitely extended, is to make his existence, if not conditional upon the physical world, at least coterminous with its duration. No such procedure is acceptable to Christian theology.

But if we abandon the concept of God as existing *in* time, is it possible to say that he existed *before* the beginning of time and will still exist *after* the end of time? Not if the scale of time is of infinite extent, for such a scale would include all conceivable times however remote. Nor is it possible if we adopt the alternative cosmological view which makes the material universe finite in time. If time came into existence with the universe and will cease if and when the universe ceases to exist, it becomes meaningless to speak of God's existence before or after the total span of the time-process. However the cosmologists eventually resolve the problem of the infinity of the time-scale, theologians can resolve their problem only by insisting that God in his own being is utterly distinct from the time-process. There is no instant of time, however remote in past or future, at which God does not exist *independently* of the temporal order. Only so can we secure the inalienable rights of the Creator in relation to his creation. Only so can we safe-guard the unique unchanging character of God in relation to the created order, which is the essential biblical meaning on the phrase, 'from everlasting to everlasting'. St Augustine was right when he said, 'Nor dost Thou by time precede time.'[1] There is no escaping this conclusion.

Nevertheless, Platonic ideas of eternity still encounter con-siderable sales-resistance from biblical theologians. Their dilemma is well illustrated by some words in which Marsh[2] comments on the views of Cullmann: 'However right we may be to reject Platonic notions of eternity as a "nunc stans" we cannot, consistently with the New Testament, ascribe limita-tions of successiveness to *God's time*; and that means that we cannot think of God's "time" or his "eternity" as endless duration.' I agree entirely that we cannot ascribe 'limitations of successiveness' to God, and that his eternal being must not be conceived as 'endless duration'. This is precisely what I have argued above. But what then is the meaning of '*God's time*'? It is an empty phrase, devoid of significance. Such writing fails to recognize that time is the experience of successiveness, and that continuing successiveness is known as duration. Where there is no successiveness (i.e. no objective physical change) it is wholly illegitimate to speak of time. If we are to make theology viable, we must take the meaning of eternity to exclude all time reference. If we are to do justice to scriptural revelation, consistently with our modern understanding, our first task is to formulate empirically the character of eternity as a non-temporal mode of existence.

THE SIMULTANEITY OF THE ETERNAL

In attempting to clear up a confusion in terminology, a legacy of the partial fusion of the Greek and Hebrew traditions, we have taken as basic the kind of religious experience which leads us to speak of the eternal; but in clarifying the issue we are led to a definition of eternity which is essentially negative. It is the

---

[1] Augustine, *Confessions*, Bk. XI, 13.
[2] J. Marsh, *The Fulness of Time*, 181 (my italics).

mode of being which is time-*less* and *un*-changing. Nor can our formulation be other than negative, for our day-to-day experience of the eternal is at best fleeting and half-understood. It is that which is wholly other than the temporal order to which we belong. Consequently a definition in terms of difference is the only possibility open to us. In much the same way, and for corresponding reasons, classical theology was driven to express all the divine attributes in negative terms.

The application of I. T. Ramsey's[1] analysis of religious language in terms of models and qualifiers was perfectly straight-forward in the case of the more naïve word 'everlasting'. What help can it give us towards an understanding of the essentially negative definition of eternity? We start from our experience of time, characterized by the fact of change all around us. We observe that some things change less than others; that persons change relatively little in their essential character; that the more perfect the character the more immune a person is to change. Then our religious experience of divine personality requires the logically infinite jump which recognizes that absolute perfection of character does not change at all. It is as though time itself has stood still—for God as he is known to us: as though change, which is the background of all other experience, has ceased. 'Changing' is a characteristic of practically all that we know, a model word which can describe even persons. Suitably qualified by a negative prefix it serves to characterize the Reality which we know in our religious experience. Or again, 'time' is an elusive phenomenon which conditions our common experience, the artistic and the poetic to a lesser degree, moral goodness hardly at all. Qualified by a negative suffix it serves to characterize our experience of the ultimate Reality who makes himself known to us in what we call religion. In either case a word which is appropriate to experience in general is given a queer logical placing; thereby it becomes suitable currency for the description of a particular and all-important kind of experience, which transcends matter-of-fact characterization.

So much for the negative aspect of our definition. The empirical approach to the problem now requires that we set down clearly what any formulation of eternity must safe-

[1] I. T. Ramsey, *Religious Language*, Chapter II.

guard, if it is to be true to the facts of biblical and Christian experience:

(1) That God can be known by finite beings in the temporal order; or, to put it in the way which preserves the divine initiative, that God who inhabits eternity is able to communicate spiritual truth to the minds of men. (Doctrine of revelation.)

(2) That the temporal order owes its existence to the divine activity (Doctrine of creation); that the temporal order exists to fulfil divine purpose; and that without divine assistance it consistently fails to do so. (Doctrine of redemption.)

(3) Though the eternal mode of being is sovereign and self-sufficient, and the temporal mode dependent and contingent, that in history the Eternal has entered into the temporal. (Doctrine of the Incarnation.)

Thus there must be an absolute distinction between the two modes of being, and also relatedness between them. By contrasting the essentially unchanging with that which is subject to change, we shall certainly maintain the absolute distinction between eternity and time. The only danger is that we may find it difficult to safeguard the relatedness. Indeed, this has been a chief objection from the Christian standpoint to the taking of Platonic ideas into the theological system; in particular that we may endanger that element of relatedness which we express in the doctrine of the Incarnation.[1] The danger must be faced: it can be resolved only as we proceed.[2] At present I shall be content to place the emphasis on the absolute distinction between the eternal and the temporal, for this is the *sine qua non* of any progress in comprehension. As Brabant[3] remarks, 'no one who does not see clearly the separation between the Divine and the human can hope to understand how they are connected'.

If anyone should raise the question of the 'where' and the 'when' of the eternal world which we postulate, I reply that it is meaningless. Our experience in religion is of a God everywhere and always present. Omnipresence in space and time is a

---

[1] W. Temple, *Nature, Man and God*, 436.   [2] See Chapter XIII.
[3] F. H. Brabant, *Time and Eternity in Christian Thought*, 33.

necessary corollary of a non-spatial, non-temporal, mode of being; and also the basic condition of relationship or relatedness between the two orders. God and eternity are neither outside nor inside the spatio-temporal world, but alongside.[1] Indeed the key-word in speaking of the relation between the temporal and the eternal is 'simultaneity'. In normal speech two occurrences are said to be simultaneous if we apprehend them at the same time, i.e. together. And our apprehension of God in his unchanging character partakes of this quality of sameness, simultaneity. 'Jesus Christ, the same yesterday, and today, and for ever' mediates this apprehension at its most intimate level. We know that *we* move forward in time. But God as apprehended in our religious experience does not. The God of today's experience is 'simultaneous' with the God of yesterday's experience. He is, and always will be, simultaneous with our constantly changing 'now': utterly distinct, neither outside nor inside our world, but alongside and known.

Having put the matter in these terms, we are in a position to consider the possible modes of mutual knowledge between a mind in time and Mind in the eternal order. That knowledge is possible at all from our side is of course a consequence of the revealing activity of the Godhead. We admit that initiative is on the side of deity: all religious experience points that way. We admit that the possibility of knowledge of the eternal by the temporal is unexpected on *a priori* grounds; but we cannot deny the fact that God has made himself known to us, and consequently that God in his eternal being has intimate knowledge of us. This is an empirical fact of revealed religion. The mode of such mutual knowledge differs according as we consider it from one side or the other. Our knowledge of the eternal has been sufficiently indicated already as regards its mode, if not its content. But what can we say about God's knowledge of us? Obviously not much—except that he knows all. Yet as regards the mode of his perfect knowledge we can, and must, say something; and this something is all-important. The clue is the concept of simultaneity. The eternal 'now' is to be thought of as strictly contemporaneous with every successive 'now' of our temporal existence and experience.

[1] J. A. T. Robinson (*Honest to God*, 11–18) makes unnecessarily heavy weather of this concept.

A diagram (Fig. 4) will illustrate rather roughly the concept which is expressed in the previous sentence. The dotted line indicates our existence in the temporal order; or alternatively, the total successiveness of the created process. Its representation as a linear series of dots is equivalent to the division of the time-scale into a succession of indefinitely short intervals, each of which may be thought of as a present moment, a 'now'. The time-scale of human experience advances from left to right, as we advance temporally through successive moments *J, K, L,* etc. At each moment our knowledge of God is of God as he eternally *is* in the non-temporal order, in so far

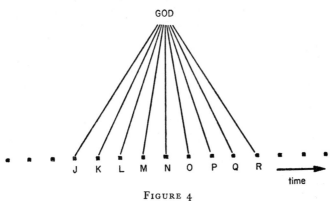

FIGURE 4

as he graciously discloses himself to our experience. This knowledge is the content of a temporal series of apprehensions of unchanging eternal reality, successively received. God's knowledge of us, by contrast, is non-temporal, non-successive. His knowledge of us at *J* is simultaneous with his knowledge of us at *K, L, M,* etc. In the temporal order, to which our conscious existence is confined, we experience change: we choose, we act, we undergo all those subtle changes which are the stuff of life. He changes not, yet knows all; and knows it simultaneously. Every instant of our successive existence is permanently and constantly within the knowledge of deity. 'Eternity is the simultaneous and complete possession of infinite life . . . God views everything as though it were taking place in the present'.[1]

---

[1] F. H. Brabant, *Time and Eternity in Christian Thought,* 64 f, quoting from Boethius. Cf. also R. G. Swinburne, *The Timelessness of God,* in *Church Quarterly Review,* CLXVI, 323–335 and 472–486 (1965).

To put the truth of the matter in another way and to illustrate it by analogy, we can imagine a cinematograph film of
our own movements and activity to be unrolled and viewed in a
single act of knowing. What for us were successive moments in a
temporal process are 'seen' and known simultaneously,
unitively, from the side of the eternal, somewhat as the film is
seen when unrolled. In one important respect the analogy
breaks down, for a film cannot be seen until after it has been
developed, and this corresponds to further passage of time. By
contrast, we must say that God 'sees' and knows while the film
is still being exposed; that he knows what was (past), what is
(present), and what will be (future), all in his own simultaneous
present. Even so the analogy, though imperfect, is useful as an
illustration of the mode of an eternal knowledge of the temporal
order. It brings out the essential character of knowledge for
Being which is not subject to the limitation of the temporal
process; for whom successiveness, with its corresponding fragmentation of knowledge and experience, does not exist. All
highly tentative no doubt, but none the less implicit in the
concept of the eternal as timeless.

It is necessary now to safeguard further the changelessness
of God in the context of his apprehension of the temporal order.
For the eternal mode of knowing is in sharp contrast with the
temporal. We are changed by the activity of knowing, i.e. by
learning: God is not. The difference may be approached by
noticing one more particular in which the analogy of the cine-
film is defective: indeed the diagram is defective too. The
time-process is represented as a succession of discrete moments
or instantaneous exposures, thereby glossing over the continuity
of temporal experience.[1] But, we may ask, What is it in our
experience that is responsible for the sense of continuity? The
answer in part is contained in the word 'memory'. What I am
or do at J, I remember at K, L, M, etc. Indeed, from a psychological point of view we should have to admit that memory
plays an important part in the sense of continuing personal
identity through changing circumstances and activities. In
other words, what I remember of my past I carry into my

---

[1] A. P. Shepherd (*The Eternity of Time*, 31–36) criticizes J. W. Dunne's use of
the same analogy, on the ground that it destroys the continuity of temporal
experience. This defect is remedied in the next chapter.

present. What is imprinted by the past on my sub-conscious I carry into the present. Quite apart from bodily changes in time, or bodily injuries carried into the present, the temporal sequence superposes change on identity. I am the same person, yet not quite the same person. What I learn at J remains with me at K. I am changed by the fact of knowing. This is what we have in mind when we speak of a person 'growing in experience.' His experience perhaps is held to qualify him for responsibilities which previously he could not have undertaken. In virtue of wider experience he is in some sense a different person: change is superposed on identity.

Now this subtle modification of the knower by the act of knowing may be thought of as a consequence of the finiteness of our knowledge; for if knowledge is finite, it is possible to learn more, and to be changed in the learning. But is it finiteness as such that is significant here? Finiteness of knowledge is a pre-condition of learning more; but it is learning that changes the knower. And since we learn progressively, in successive steps, we must think of the modification of the knower as a consequence of the temporal mode of his existence. The contrast between ourselves and God in this respect is now clear. Where all knowing is timeless rather than successive, and the wholeness of knowledge is held consequently in a single simultaneity, there can be no change of the knower by the act of knowing. The changelessness of God, which is an essential though negatively-stated attribute in classical theology, is the logical accompaniment of his eternal mode of existence. This impossibility of change in deity will be found to have highly significant consequences for the Christian doctrine of creation, and for the proper understanding of the Incarnation and the Atonement. For though creation, revelation, and redemption are divine activities which change conditions in the temporal order, no Christian thinker could agree that God himself is changed by such activity. This, I believe, is what Brabant[1] has in mind when he asserts that the 'conception of an Activity without Change is of the utmost importance in the Christian idea of Eternity.'

We began by posing the question of the relative legitimacy of

[1] F. H. Brabant, *Time and Eternity in Christian Thought*, 22.

two competing conceptions of 'eternity'; the one reducing to a mode of existence still strictly temporal, even though indefinitely extended; the other of an entirely different quality, because timeless. For the sake of securing a sufficiently wide world-view, comprising the truth of revealed religion consistently with philosophy and the more recent developments in natural science, we have recognized the necessity of the latter view. Just as the temporal process is characterized essentially by change, so the eternal world is to be conceived in terms of the absence of change. That which is eternal is everlasting, for it *is* at all conceivable times: but that which is everlasting within the limited temporal perspective of scripture is not necessarily eternal. Yet the doctrine of creation implies that in some sense the divine must 'antedate' the whole temporal order. In the last analysis therefore, the conception of a timeless eternity as the mode of being of deity is not so much the taking on board of an alien philosophical idea as the logical requirement of the empirical approach to theological problems; which, starting from the biblical evidence, seeks a rational expression of the truth which is there revealed. It remains to test the formulation of eternity which we have outlined. In order that it may be serviceable to theology, it must satisfy fully the empirical conditions already set out. We proceed in the following chapters to consider further the doctrine of creation as the expression of divine purpose, and the conditions which createdness imposes on human freedom. This in turn leads to a discussion of revelation through the divine control of history, and finally to the doctrine of the Incarnation; which, lying at the heart of Christianity, expresses the ultimate relatedness of the temporal and the eternal orders.

X

ETERNITY AND CREATION

THE created order is related to the Creator as a work of art
to a creative artist. This assertion secures the dependence of
the universe upon its Creator, and is analogically equivalent to
the classical theological statement of the problem of existence.
From the point of view of modern Christian thought it has the
advantage of being more fruitful than arid metaphysical
definition. The search for a suitable form of the analogy led us
to turn away from the static arts to the drama; in which time
and the temporal development of character are integral ingredients. Moreover, the inalienable autonomy of the *dramatis
personae*, recognized by human dramatists as imposing real
limitations on the freedom of their creator, seemed to point to a
further facet of the created order, namely the existence of free-
will. Thus, the only fully adequate form of the analogy is one
which sees the Creator as the Dramatist who expresses himself
in the drama of creative process.

In order to fill out this picture we must now bear in mind the
insights which have occupied our attention in the previous
two chapters. (1) Time, as the subjective apprehension of
change, is in no sense a universal characteristic of the external
world. The theory of relativity has shown that clock-time stands
in a peculiar and hitherto unsuspected relation to the rest of our
sense experience. Consistent representation of external reality
is possible only in terms of the four-dimensional space-time
continuum appropriate to particular inertial frames of reference.
(2) On the other hand eternity, as the realm to which the being
of Almighty God belongs, must be thought of in terms of timelessness. Or rather, since God in his own essential being is
unchanging, his apprehension of all else that exists must be
thought of as partaking of simultaneity. Only so can we secure

the infinite disparity between the divine mode of apprehension and our own. We must therefore attempt to integrate our science, our philosophy, and our theology into a unified view of the creative process: an ambitious programme which may be only partially fulfilled.

RELATIVITY AND THE ETERNAL

It might be supposed that Einstein's theory has little direct bearing upon philosophical theology. For is it not a highly abstract mathematical construction devised to deal with specific problems in mechanics, and such like fields? True, it was anomalies of this character which led to its formulation; but once propounded its results were seen to be more far-reaching. Nothing less than the possibility of valid conceptual knowledge of the external world is at stake; and Einstein's work is a re-examination of our intuitive ideas. Relativity is essentially epistemological. It is concerned with the meaning of sense observation; and inevitably therefore it bears upon every discipline which claims to say anything about external reality. Time as experienced is subjective. But any statement about time implies at least the possibility of an observation of some time-keeping device, such as a clock. In a universe in which no information can travel faster than light, the meaning to be attached to a temporal observation is by no means obvious. Common sense turns out to be no guide at all. It appears that a temporal reference is merely a piece of information subjectively detached from the space-time continuum, relative to which all the sense experience of an observer is properly co-ordinated. The space-time continuum alone is adequate to represent external reality: the detachment of a particular element leads to inconsistency, and is logically indefensible in the conceptual characterization of reality.

That we can get along well enough with our ordinary conception of time for day-to-day purposes is the consequence of two facts which belong to our normally parochial outlook: (a) the fact that we are concerned with a relatively small portion of the universe, and (b) that our motion is invariably small compared with the velocity of light. Any adequate philosophical approach to external reality must divest itself of these limitations as they affect the reference of physical process to the temporal concept. There is no such thing as universal time. The 'discovery' of the space-time continuum implies a necessary sophistication of our common-sense view of events as located in space and happening in time. It is a representational device required of us as we stretch our human thinking to the utmost, in order to comprehend and rationalize our sense experience. This is its scientific or philosophical status. But what is its status in relation to the eternal order? This now is a question on which theology can claim to be heard.

The Christian doctrine of creation teaches among other things that man is made in the divine image. One consequence of this is that man bears a distant resemblance to his Creator in the possession of a mind, with its powers of analysis and conceptualization. Without doubt this is an exceedingly bold claim, yet integral to the Christian position; and its truth is implicit in the development of doctrine. It is a principle which will prove serviceable in considering the theological status of space-time; but it is well to illustrate its application in a more familiar connection, before looking at our specific problem. Consider then the logical stages by which we approach the doctrine of the Holy Trinity. Briefly, so the argument goes, God has revealed himself to us in three modes, logically distinguishable, and pointing to three co-existing characters (*hypostases*) in the Divine as experienced. Doctrine arrives at the 'Economic Trinity': a human apprehension of the Godhead as he has revealed himself, and as we have rationalized our experience of revelation. This is the empirical stage in the formulation of doctrine, to which reference was made earlier. Then Christian theology makes the final step from the 'economic' to the 'essential' Trinity, justifying its procedure on the grounds: (*a*) that God's self-revelation must be true to his own reality, since he is the God of truth; and (*b*) that human minds, admittedly puny, are akin to divine Mind, and therefore able to apprehend the truth of God's essential being, even though inadequately.[1] The two stages of the argument, though sometimes glossed over in the manuals, are logically necessary; and a quite essential part is played by the assertion of faith

[1] See K. E. Kirk in *Essays on the Trinity and the Incarnation* (ed. A. E. J. Rawlinson), 237.

that a real resemblance exists between finite and infinite minds.

We are justified in proceeding along somewhat similar lines in the present case. If the human mind is distantly akin to the divine Mind, it follows that our representation of external reality, once it is self-consistent in regard to fact and logic, bears some real resemblance to the truth of the external world as it is perfectly known by its Creator. This means that the space-time continuum may be regarded as a valid representation of the external world as apprehended by Deity. No doubt, as in the analogous case of trinitarian doctrine, the correspondence is imperfect. It may be held that the imperfection is the greater since the argument is based in the first instance on the deliverances of reason rather than on revelation. Yet we are justified, tentatively at least, in making the step from the 'economic' to the 'essential' characterization of the external world. There is, of course, a significant difference between the human and the divine apprehension of the external world. The human view is arrived at only by an exacting and deliberate process of sophistication. For the divine Mind we must presume that apprehension in something like space-time terms is immediate; since we are suggesting that this *is* the eternal, unchanging, representation of the external world and its motions.[1] The human mind naturally detaches the spatial and temporal co-ordinates from one another, since it experiences the world from the inside as changing and successive. The divine Mind is under no such necessity. We must therefore presume that God knows all, and knows it immediately, in a manner analogous to the non-temporal representation which we arrive at only by the rigorous application of reason.

Regarding space-time representation as akin to the eternal apprehension of created reality, we begin to see the significance of the world-points and world-lines of relativity theory. A world-point is a non-temporal representation in four dimensions of an event, which we apprehend as occurring at a particular

---

[1] O. C. de Beauregard in his recent study of Relativity (*La Notion de Temps*, 201–207) endorses the view that 'Le continuum spatio-temporel, donné dans sa totalité, fait descendre du ciel sur la terre le vieux thème métaphysique d'un univers donné, dans sa durée totale, *sub specie aeternitatis*': i.e. he recognizes space-time representation as the equivalent of the eternal apprehension of external reality.

point in space and at a particular instant of time. It is therefore the immediate apprehension of that event from the point of view of eternity. Similarly a world-line, which is the non-temporal representation in four dimensions of a succession of events in the continuing existence of an individual entity in the external world, is the eternal and unchanging apprehension of that entity and the motions which it undergoes. What we experience temporally and spatially is apprehended unitively from the stand-point of eternity, in a form which includes temporality under an unchanging aspect. It follows that the dotted line of the time axis in Figure 4 is properly to be thought of as the world-line of a stationary human being, as apprehended from the eternal world. God 'sees' all at once, for the representation in space-time is strictly non-temporal: whereas we, immersed in the continuum, see point-events successively, and apprehend God in his unchanging being at successive points of the time-line, i.e. at succeeding instants of our own (subjective) temporal experience.

The significance of relativity concepts from the point of view of philosophical theology has now become clear. The world-lines of the space-time continuum, which correspond to changes and motions of the entities comprising the material world, are essentially a non-temporal representation of external reality. They partake of an eternal character, since they are timeless and unchanging. In a remarkable way, relativity therefore supports the view which we have developed already of the relation between time and eternity. Indeed, the theory gives formal character to our idea of the divine apprehension of the created order. The status of space-time is that of the eternal view of the material universe, no less: and its ultimate significance for philosophical theology is immense.

THE CREATION OF THE TEMPORAL

It is abundantly clear that the character imposed upon the created order is one of change, rather than of permanence. True, the fundamental particles composing the material universe are for the most part relatively stable; though some of those quite recently discovered have life-times of a mere fraction of a second. Nevertheless, the configuration of the material components of the universe is constantly changing; and even such solid-looking objects as the earth have no permanence when considered over the longest vistas of time. Change rather than permanence is the essential characteristic of the created order: change moreover in a particular direction, from a more ordered to a less ordered statistical state. The direction of time's arrow is that of the unidirectional change of entropy, both in our own bodily organisms and in the world at large. This fact, as we have seen, appears to be the physical basis of time as a subjective apprehension; as indeed it is the pre-condition of temporal observation. Though we are forbidden to postulate a universal time, yet the time-concept remains meaningful for a restricted portion of the universe. And since we are confined to a restricted portion, knowing comparatively little of more remote regions, we are entitled to examine the status and significance of time as such in the theological view of the universe as a created order.

What do we really mean by the statement that change takes place in the direction specified by the phrase '*from* order *to* disorder'? The prepositions imply the recognition of the later in relation to the earlier. How is this relationship either known or defined? *From* and *to* are meaningful only to that sense of time which is logically prior to any discussion of disorder or entropy. If we are to avoid circularity, all we can say is that our own experience within the created order *is* temporal experience. We are immersed in temporality, so that the time-sense is both given and primary. What physical science accomplishes in this connection is the correlation of the time-sense (qualitatively, and perhaps quantitatively) with entropy change, as a fact of nature on the macroscopic scale, discernible to a developed scientific insight. We have offered not an explanation of the character of sense experience, strictly speaking, but an alternative and highly sophisticated description of temporality. Entropy-change is the physical correlate of that temporality which is disclosed as the condition of creaturely existence. In creating a world which should be temporal, and in which conscious creatures should live creaturely lives, the first requirement (physically speaking) is that the creative act should secure the fact of the degradation of energy, as expressed in the law of entropy.

Temporality is inherent in the external order as such, and not merely in our subjective human experience. The material world, or at least that portion of it to which we belong, is 'running down' as a clock runs down; and this fact constitutes its temporal aspect. Man, who belongs to the material order even while transcending it, shares in its temporality both objectively and in his subjective experience. The created order, as a *created* order, is characterized by entropy change. If God had created a universe *not* subject to the law of entropy, such a world would have been non-temporal; that is to say, it would have shared in the eternal mode of being proper to God himself. Such a world may exist for all we know: but emphatically it is not *this* world. Possibly the world of pure created spirits is so constituted. Aquinas[1] held that the angels experience a quasi-temporal existence, the *aevum*, in which growth and decay are excluded, but to whose activity a 'before' and 'after' are conjoined. Such speculations are hypothetical in the extreme. We are embodied, materially, and what we do know from careful investigation of the laws of nature is that the created order to which we belong is subject to unidirectional entropy change. Such change is inherent in the material order as such, and constitutes its temporality.

The status of time in relation to the creation is now clear. Temporality is the distinguishing feature of the created order as we know it. This is the theological significance of time. And the understanding of temporality at which we have arrived ties up remarkably well with the existential approach to questions of ontology. As Heidegger[2] insists, being (for us) is 'being towards an end'. *Dasein* 'is not "temporal" because it "stands in history", but . . . it exists historically . . . only because it is temporal in the very basis of its Being'. It is clear of course from the tone of the whole treatment that Heidegger uses the word 'end' to denote not a goal or fulfilment but a finishing. Existential philosophy is not teleological. It is restricted in its outlook to this world order and its temporal perspective. Less than Christian, it needs to be supplemented before it can

---

[1] See F. H. Brabant, *Time and Eternity in Christian Thought*, 74 ff. Personally I believe that the whole discussion of 'time' is vitiated where the material conditions of temporality are absent. Aquinas was not to know this however.

[2] M. Heidegger, *Being and Time*, 428.

provide an adequate world-view for theological thinking. But as far as it goes, it stands in general agreement with what we assert to be the significance and status of time.

We have insisted however that time, as we experience it, is a component of the space-time continuum, subjectively detached; and we have regarded space-time representation as the eternal aspect of this world order. If also the time component is based upon, or correlated with, entropy change, what does this imply from the point of view of eternity? Must we not say that the law of entropy change is somehow inherent in the four-dimensional dependent being with which this world order is creatively endowed? Christian doctrine is accustomed to think of God as Sustainer as well as Creator. To say that this world order is sustained in existence, however, does not add anything from the point of view of eternity; since the temporal element belongs to our experience, not to God's. From the standpoint of eternity the temporality of the created universe is a secondary consequence of the structure which is given to it and apprehended non-temporally, i.e. simultaneously.

The simultaneity of the creative act, in relation to the process of temporal change so initiated, may be exhibited rather vividly by a slight adaption of the previous diagram. The created order is a succession of existing states, or discrete events, each one of which is to be referred causally (directly or indirectly) to the creative will. The creative will belongs however to the world of unchanging eternal reality. Thus, the creative act, single and unique in the eternal mode, 'spreads out', so to speak, into the multiplicity of existences in time and throughout time. Christian theology, following the language of Genesis i, has often expressed itself by saying that God utters his creative *word*, so bringing into being all that exists. Now a *word*, though its utterance occupies a short interval of time, can be thought of as non-temporal. It is complete in itself, unchanging; and, relative to the extent of created time, instantaneous. The divine *word* is the cause of creation. Its effect however is the complete range of temporal existents and events. It 'spreads out' as created reality under the conditions of time. Our distinction between the eternal and the temporal therefore secures the existence and sustenance of the whole created order, throughout time, as the effect of a single creative act, the *word* or *fiat* of God. (See

Figure 5.) There is no necessity for us to think of fresh acts of creation, during the course of time. All that comes into existence at any time forms part of the logical nexus, or continuing process, created *in its entirety* by a single act of the divine will.

If the Artist analogy of creative activity is to be serviceable, from the stand-point of eternity it seems to require an art-form which is apprehended non-temporally. Does this conflict with what has been said already, about the supreme usefulness of the dramatic analogy? Not if we are careful to safeguard the

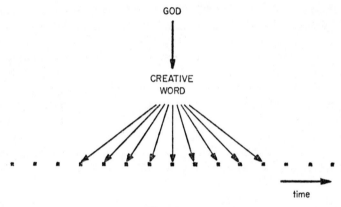

FIGURE 5

distinction between the temporal and the eternal. Those art-forms which can be apprehended non-temporally in our experience are static patterns in two or three dimensions—typically, painting and sculpture. The word 'pattern', which covers all the static arts known to us, is used advisedly; for it is the clue that leads the mind from the world of two or three spatial dimensions to the fuller world of the four-dimensional continuum. The complex of world-lines, which is the eternal view of the created universe and its processes, can be thought of as a 'pattern' in four dimensions. By the creative act it is given in its wholeness. and apprehended in simultaneity. From our point of view however, immersed as we are in temporality and conditioned by it, the 'pattern' is apprehended as developing purpose, i.e. dramatically. Thus, the Dramatist analogy is the temporal form, appropriate to our condition, of an artistic

L

'patterning' of the whole created order as it is apprehended from the stand-point of eternity. What is to us the time dimension is given, along with the spatial dimensions, in a single creative act, which is the supreme artistry of the Creator.

Seen from within the temporal process however, the fact of the degradation of energy, the movement from order to disorder, is not easy to reconcile immediately with the concept of creative purpose. We do not naturally conceive of purpose in terms of a general tendency towards increasing disorderliness: indeed, rather the reverse. Presumably this is the fundamental reason why the sense of divine purpose, as characterizing the processes of this world order, is not self-evident; and why, apart from supernatural grace and Christian faith, a teleological view is untenable by most men. Pattern is not immediately apparent; as those who employ the teleological argument in its usual form always discover. Pattern becomes apparent only when we learn to view the world process *sub specie aeternitatis*.

But consider instead how the four-dimensional continuum appears from the stand-point of eternity. Its almost infinite number of criss-cross lines, the world-lines of all existing material particles, is apprehended in somewhat the same way as we view a pen-and-ink drawing. In an etching every stroke of the pen is in its place: in relation to the others each single stroke makes its contribution; and the whole is a meaningful picture, a work of art. I am not suggesting that *any* array of criss-cross lines constitutes a pattern. Of course it does not. But we recognize that an example of this particular art-form is still a work of art even though it is made up in detail of criss-cross lines. In other words, the presence of apparent randomness in detail is not inconsistent with an over-all patterning. Such randomness of line in the eternal view of the created world is to be correlated with statistical disorder, and its temporal increase, as seen from within the continuum, and is not necessarily a negation of purpose. There is not the slightest need to regard increasing randomness at the microscopic level as the work of an evil power—plenty of room remains at a higher level of being for the activity of evil; and it is precisely at that higher level of conscious choice that we recognize evil. There is no case for postulating the influence of evil in the characteristic properties of matter itself. What we have called the 'randomness' of criss-cross lines is part and parcel of the over-all pattern imposed by the Creator upon the creation; and from the point of view of physical science this is statistical disorder increasing temporally. If an etching is viewed under a magnifying glass, the texture undoubtedly appears random. Yet if it is truly a work of art, every line is in the right place. The pattern is seen only when it is viewed as a whole. And we may believe that the same is true of the created universe, as it is apprehended from the standpoint of eternity.

The purposive view of creation is not therefore at variance with our modern understanding of physical process: nor is it a piece of wishful thinking imposed by us upon external reality. In fact, consideration of relativity and the entropy law enables us to grasp more easily the truth that from the point of view of eternity the created world is patterned; and that its patterning in the minutest detail is the ground-work which secures the fulfilment of purpose in temporality. Words put into the mouth of Lazarus by Dorothy Sayers[1] admirably illustrate the point of view which I have tried to develop on more abstract lines. '*This* life is like weaving at the back of the loom. All you see is the crossing of the threads. In *that* life you go round to the front and see the wonder of the pattern.' . . . 'What sort of pattern is it?' . . . 'Beautiful and terrible. And—how can I tell you?—it is *familiar*. You have known it from all eternity. For He that made it is the form of all things, Himself both the weaver and the loom.' Here is the essential idea, expressed in the vividness of dramatic form; though perhaps not with full theological accuracy, particularly in the final phrases. Yet, 'Beautiful and terrible'—the pattern in its wholeness is something more than the world-lines of material entities. It includes love, and evil overcome by love.

TEMPORALITY AND ETERNITY IN PERSONAL LIFE

The Christian doctrine of creation is concerned less with things than with persons. In terms of the Dramatist analogy, the creation of the world of inanimate matter ranks only as the setting of the stage: the drama, properly so-called, begins with the creation of living things, and becomes significant with the

[1] Dorothy Sayers, *The Man born to be King*, 214.

creation of man. Or, in terms of that form of the analogy which is appropriate to the eternal world, human history marks the significant part of the pattern; all that precedes it in time the background. In either form of the analogy, the creation of man in the divine image, and the total span of human history under divine control, are the supreme achievement of creative activity. As we already recognize, the 'image' consists in the possession of mental and spiritual faculties, a distant kinship with the Creator. And human nature is fulfilled in that fellowship with God which includes the knowledge of the Truth, and the response of love and adoration.

At this point the capabilities of the inanimate creation are totally transcended. Humble in origin, of the earth earthy, man is capable of knowledge and creaturely response to which the laws of nature provide no clue. Yet as a complex of body, mind, and spirit he is firmly rooted in lower nature, unable to resist its laws, utterly dependent on physical necessities, limited, temporal, finite. Though his being here is towards an end (*telos*), man is an embodied creation, and the shackles of the flesh weigh heavily upon him till death apparently ends all. Are we then to regard mind and spirit, as they are manifested in embodied forms, as mere epiphenomena of the material order? To do so would be implicitly to account for the higher in terms of the lower. Scientific explanation can do no other. Theological interpretation must needs reverse the procedure.[1] If an adequate account of human nature is to be given, we must start with the Creator whose 'image' is to be recognized at an otherwise unexpected point in the created process. So far from being mere epiphenomena, mind and spirit are the culminating achievement of creation, which give meaning to all that went before in time.

Yet even if personality is to be interpreted in terms of the Creator rather than in terms of the lower creation, our conceptual difficulties are not at an end. We say that man is in the image of God, that he has faculties distantly akin to the divine. But in what sense can human faculties grounded in

---

[1] The account from below (explanation) is fully valid, but only half the truth. It needs to be supplemented by the account from above (interpretation), which also is fully valid but only half the truth. Both halves are necessary. Neither must be overlooked.

temporal existence be even remotely akin to the *Eternal?* Are we not driven to recognize something potentially eternal in man himself, immersed though he is in temporal process? It would be unjustifiable to assert that in the possession of mind and spirit man shares consciously here and now in the eternal world; for experience follows experience, and apprehension and knowledge partake of successiveness. But to say that human mind and spirit are potentially eternal is to look beyond present limitations to what can rightly be called a goal (*telos*). For this Christian faith gives us warrant. The Christian hope is eternal life: we need not deny to the adjective its full meaning.

Approaching the same problem from the psychological point of view, A. P. Shepherd[1] would have us see human personality as an entity which is truly eternal already, though its conscious experience is confined to the temporal. He asserts that 'our real human personality is continually being constructed out of its continuous experience in contact with the physical world, every such experience being woven into the fabric of its real being'. The past is not to be 'regarded as "dead and gone", but rather as a living articulated whole of experience, extending right up to the ever-changing "present", whose successive experiences continually add to that articulated whole'. The real self, however, is 'not as such self-conscious, its self-consciousness being limited to its point of direct contact with the physical world'. Further analysis of the mode of human knowledge and of reflection on past experience leads Shepherd to write: 'My mental construct is an activity of the self and the hypothesis I submit is that as such it is an eternal element in the self, persisting when the external material reality, which originally provoked and conditioned it, exists no longer.' Indeed, he suggests that '*all the experience of a self is its own eternal possession, inherent in itself*'.[2] Now without necessarily endorsing all that Shepherd says about the inclusion of the temporal within the eternal (which is his main thesis), we can accept the point he makes here as a valid contribution. This life and its experience creates the self which we shall take into the world to come. However, we should hesitate to describe the *self* as actually eternal during the period of its temporal experience. That which is still growing, and whose components are still in strict

[1] A. P. Shepherd, *The Eternity of Time*, 25 f.   [2] *loc. cit.*, 47 (his italics).

temporal order, can hardly be eternal already. Let us say then that in our present temporal existence we build up a self whose depth is *potentially* eternal. This suggestion still makes room for eternal life in the Johannine sense as a present reality, and lays the foundation for the persistence of personality beyond bodily death, in fulfilment of the Christian hope.

Here and now, however, the potentially eternal image is 'subjected to vanity'. We are truly immersed in the temporal order; subject to the law of entropy and all its consequences, including bodily dissolution. But as Christians we live by faith in the Resurrection, sharing proleptically in the Risen Life. We can accept that our present being is 'towards an end', because in faith we see our 'end' as also a liberation of the potentially eternal image from the bond of temporality imposed by the law of entropy. Is this not precisely what St Paul is saying in Romans 8, verses 18–25: deliverance 'from the bondage of corruption into the liberty of the glory of the children of God'?

But is there not also a sense in which temporality as such remains ingrained in the potentially eternal image? Should we not perhaps conceive the after-life, when the image is liberated, as including temporality in the sense of successiveness of apprehension and knowledge: a sort of 'hang-over' from earthly life and its truly temporal conditioning? I cannot help thinking that the Christian hope implies some such conception, difficult though it may be. For how can the human soul at death be ready for an existence which is truly eternal, and hence by definition no longer subject to change of any kind? We can hardly avoid the view that human personality requires a progressive purification in the after-life. Any realistic assessment of our status in relation to the Eternal logically implies some continuation of successiveness, albeit under totally different and quite inconceivable conditions.

The Christian doctrine of the resurrection of the body, to which admittedly it is difficult to give precision without verging on the naïve, seems to point in the same direction; indicating the possession of faculties of some kind, through which we can know and be known, and which can be represented analogically by the concept of a 'body'. 'For now we see in a mirror, darkly; but then face to face: now I know in part; but then shall I know (fully) even as also I have been known (fully).' (1 Cor. xiii. 12) In mysterious but pregnant words, the man of faith reaches out to the ultimate truth of our status as creatures redeemed in Christ and looking towards our liberation. To which little can be added this side the grave.

But if some relic of temporality remains as as essential condition of our imperfection, at least it is temporality deprived of its sting. It is no longer 'being towards an end' in Heidegger's pessimistic phrase; but 'being towards our fulfilment', with an eternal goal clearly in sight and longed for. Under the still-successive conditions which human personality cannot immediately shake off, the vision of God in his love and holiness must become ever clearer. And we can surely hazard the view that the goal is reached when the potentially eternal image, purified and perfected progressively, takes on that eternity for which it is lovingly prepared both here and hereafter. For if the image is potentially eternal, as we are led to believe, the blessedness for which we were created logically implies that the last vestiges of our temporality must be finally done away. Is this the meaning of the theology of deification in the Orthodox Church? 'Salvation is the assimilation of human nature to God.'[1] And assimilation can hardly fail to include a sharing in the mode of eternity.

[1] E. L. Mascall, *Grace and Nature in East and West, Church Quarterly Review,* CLXIV, 184 (1963).

XI

FORE-KNOWLEDGE AND FREEDOM

NOT the least difficult of our problems is the relationship between divine fore-knowledge and the *logic* of causal sequence or free choice as we know it. The one is an established tenet of the Christian religion; the other a general principle universally if implicitly accepted, notwithstanding continuing discussion between libertarian and determinist view-points. Somehow we must safeguard both aspects of the truth.

'O Lord, thou hast searched me out and known me:
Thou knowest my down-sitting and mine up-rising,
Thou understandest my thoughts long before.
Thou art about my path and about my bed:
And spiest out all my ways.
For lo, there is not a word in my tongue:
But thou, O Lord, knowest it altogether.'
(Psa. cxxxix. 1–3)

Or again, '*Omnia enim nuda et aperta sunt oculis eius, ea etiam quae libera creaturarum actione futura sunt.*'
(Vatican Council I)

No Christian would wish to deny this. Yet our understanding of the external world is based on the recognition of causal sequences, which in some sense determine observable phenomena. And human personality implies the existence of certain freedoms of willing and acting which appear logically to preclude prior prediction—except in so far as statistical methods are applicable to the behaviour patterns of large assemblages.

Where a causal sequence is confined to the order of inanimate nature, the concept of God as Infinite Mind might seem to suggest that fore-knowledge may be the outcome of fore-calculation. Adopting a position of thorough-going determinism, we might hold that a complete knowledge of the laws and the initial conditions logically includes a knowledge of the phenomenal consequences for the whole of time. This would be to conceive God as Laplace's omniscient calculator.[1] The implied degree of determinism, apparently acceptable to mathematical physicists in the nineteenth century, would not be endorsed today. Fore-calculation offers no escape from the logical impasse. Where the causal sequence involves organic life, more specifically human life, the problem is even more acute. How can we accommodate divine fore-knowledge with any real autonomy in the created order? Pious phrases devoid of content will not pass muster. We dare not answer: 'I cannot predict in advance how A will act. But my mind is only finite. God is infinite; and therefore I accept that he can predict where I cannot.' The invocation of a *deus ex machina* merely glosses over the problem.

Closely intertwined with this problem is the current debate regarding the place of causality in the determination of human conduct. Our knowledge of the relationship between the mind and the brain is still far from complete. Neither the libertarian nor the determinist is able to give a *detailed* account of how choice is exercised, though each side has valid points to make. We can admit that freedom of decision is more circumscribed sometimes than it appears to the individual who exercises it: that such freedom as we have may be inhibited in a variety of ways, biochemically, by hypnosis, etc. Yet for practical purposes we cannot break away entirely from our notion of human responsibility. A court of law, in accepting a plea of diminished responsibility, none the less upholds the concept of responsibility by implication. No doubt responsibility shades into irresponsibility, freedom of choice into mechanistic determination, in some departments of human activity. For the purpose of theoretical discussion, we can hardly avoid oscillating between two clear-cut views: one libertarian, the other determinist. That is to say, we recognize that in principle it is possible to *conceive* two accounts of human behaviour, mutually exclusive, one in terms of the sovereignty of mind, the other

1 Karl Heim, *The Transformation of the Scientific World View*, 129 f.

in terms of neuro-physiology; and though each has its whole-hearted protagonists, neither has a monopoly of truth or logic.

In order to resolve this complex of problems we must look further into the meaning of the principle of causality: first as regards its validity in relation to subjective-objective discrimination; second as regards the temporal-eternal distinction with which by now we are familiar. Then we may hope to exhibit what is commonly called 'fore-knowledge' as a characteristic of the eternal mode of apprehension in its timelessness, rather than of the infinity (as such) of Divine Mind; and the difference between libertarian and determinist views of conduct as essentially one of perspective.

CAUSALITY AND UNDERSTANDING

The causal view of phenomena is part and parcel of the temporal perspective. To the human mind, immersed in the space-time continuum, phenomena appear to be related to one another (as we say) causally; whereas space-time is essentially 'geometrical' in its manner of representation: it disguises the connectedness of events as we normally apprehend them. The obvious implication is that the status of causality is somewhat different from the stand-point of eternity. In order to understand the principle we must look rather carefully at the way we use it, and how it has grown up.

In origin it seems that causality is the explanation we offer of such occurrences as we initiate by our own personal activity. The door is open because I opened it. I am the cause of the door standing open. If we carry our minds back to pre-scientific periods of history, or to the earliest phase of our own personal development, we recognize immediately that 'cause' is a personal category, before it has any work to do in a more sophisticated approach to external phenomena. Consequently we are not surprised to discover that classical metaphysics elaborated the concept within its own world of thought, distinguishing a variety of senses in which it might be employed legitimately. A particularly clear statement of the classical position is the following:—

'There are . . . four ways in which the cause may pass into the effect . . . A man building a house is its efficient cause; it is built to afford protection from the weather, and this is its final cause; it is made of bricks and mortar, its material cause; and it is a building, and a building of a particular kind, which is its formal cause.'[1]

Now here the whole sequence of legitimate uses is an extension of the appropriateness of the first, or fundamental sense, distinguished as the efficient cause. The man himself initiates the house-building. No man, no house. But even so, if the man has no reason for building, there will be no house; if no materials for building, again no house; if no architect's drawing, or its mental equivalent, still no house. Not only the efficient cause, but also the final, the material, and the formal causes play their part in our explanation. Yet the man is primary: his activity, mental and bodily, runs through the whole project. The purpose is his purpose; the materials, what he selects in accordance with the state of his bank balance; the form, what he intends. The four senses of the word 'cause' proceed from different aspects of the man himself, as an initiating, purposive, selective, and designing person; and the above analysis is therefore regarded as explaining the activity in its whole range, from drawing-board to house-warming.

True, not many of us think naturally on these lines. Even so, it is well to have the classical picture in mind, for it is the historical background of all causal thinking. In origin, 'cause' is the personal category of explanation; in the sense that persons are recognized as causes: and this recognition is prior historically and logically to any further sophistication of the concept in philosophy or science.

The concept of causality in the scientific discussion of nature involves a further extension of the principle in a somewhat different direction. How are we to explain those occurrences in the external world for which no human agency is responsible? for example, thunderstorms, earthquakes, the weather, the growth of crops, etc. Pre-scientific man 'explained' what he did not understand in nature, to his own satisfaction if not to ours, by postulating spiritual agencies of various kinds,

[1] Quoted by E. L. Mascall, *He Who Is*, 55n, from Phillips, *Modern Thomistic Philosophy*, II, 234.

benevolent or otherwise. Primitive animism is the crudest example of this kind of reasoning; gnosticism, with its range of intermediate beings descending from God to nature, a more sophisticated version designed to come to terms with monotheism. Classical metaphysical theology is the intellectually respectable Christian version of the same explanatory technique, in which the efficient cause of all observable phenomena is held to be God himself. Following historically upon this background of philosophical achievement, the scientific study of nature made its own unique advance by recognizing phenomena themselves as the 'causes' of further phenomena; the mental scaffolding being largely discarded by practising scientists— which is a pity, for it has led to considerable confusion of thought.

This extension of the concept of 'cause' in modern scientific usage is unavoidable but none the less queer. We are saying, in effect: Rather as a person by his own choosing can initiate change in his environment, so the prior occurrence of one phenomenon (or group of phenomena) 'initiates' the occurrence of further phenomena.[1] But here, 'initiates' is no longer a purposeful word. Emptied of its meaning till it approximates to the colloquial 'triggers off', it contains two distinguishable ideas: (1) temporal order, and (2) logical necessity.

(1) The one phenomenon is found to be uniformly prior to the other in temporal order. Thus in the interest of rationalization the sense of antecedent occurrence in time is taken over from human purposiveness (where intention precedes act) so justifying the continued use of the word 'cause' in a different universe of discourse. Cause and effect are temporally related: their order in time is invariable. Where cause and effect occur in the same region of space, the time interval between them (even though it may be vanishingly small) is exhibited directly to sense. Where cause and effect occur in widely separated regions, the temporal relationship reappears as the conceptual restriction previously mentioned: namely that a phenomenon at a point P cannot be the cause of a phenomenon at another point Q unless the interval between them is equal to, or greater than,

---

[1] The isolation of phenomenal causes presupposes of course that we disregard all prior events other than those apart from which the effect is never observed to occur. The question at issue is the *status* of causes so isolated.

the time taken by light to travel through the distance PQ.[1] No physical influence can be propagated faster than a light-signal. And the influence in question must reach the point where it is to have an effect prior to the occurrence of the phenomenon caused. That science thinks in this way is the consequence of the fact that causality as a principle of explanation is connected uniquely with temporal sequence, and would be meaningless apart from this sequence. The cause-effect relationship is an account of the temporal connection between phenomena, in terms derived by analogy from the human initiation of occurrences.

(2) But observation shows that there is also a logical relationship between cause and effect. The occurrence of the phenomenon which we call the 'effect' is logically impossible until that which we call the 'cause' has created the material conditions. An obvious instance on the observable scale is the operation of clock-work; in which the movement of the pendulum to-and-fro permits the advance of the escapement tooth by tooth, under the driving force of the weight or spring. Or again, a particular stage in a chemical reaction chain can take place only when the occurrence of the previous stage has provided the necessary material substance.[2] In this sense, processes in nature appear to be mechanistic in character: we recognize logical necessity as well as pure temporal sequence in the phenomenal order as observed.

Having made the distinction however, we cannot fail to notice that the logical connectedness of events is their temporal relation in a particular aspect. The *temporal* sequence of cause and effect is the really characteristic feature of phenomenal causality. And the employment of causality as a category of explanation is an extension of the human analogy to those classes of external events which are not the direct result of human activation. Apart from antecedent priority, all other connotations of the word 'cause' are deliberately suppressed. Progress is possible in no other way. The inherent value of the

---

[1] P. W. Bridgman, *The Logic of Modern Physics*, 86.

[2] For instance, let a chain reaction proceed according to the following scheme:

$$(1)\ A + X \rightarrow B,\ (2)\ B + Y \rightarrow C,\ (3)\ C + Z \rightarrow D.$$

The production of any C is necessarily contingent on the production of any B. Similarly the production of any D is contingent on the production of any C.

scientific account of causation is that it concerns itself only with observables. From the metaphysical stand-point this is also its limitation: it takes no cognizance of 'efficient' or 'final' concepts, as classical philosophy has understood those terms. Instead, the sequence of cause and effect comes to be invested with a logic of its own; which on examination turns out to be none other than observed relatedness in temporal order. It is this temporal conditioning that characterizes scientific explanation of the external world. Such explanation is essentially a view from within time, a temporal perspective. It stands or falls with the inherent right of the human subject to a valid understanding of his objective environment. And consequently, for all its elegance, the principle of antecedent phenomenal causality cannot be pressed to the point at which it denies the sovereign status of the human person. Either we accept the scientific account of phenomena as valid for the objective world (of *it*) but not for the subjective consciousness (*I*), or we cut the ground from under our feet.

So much then for the validity of the principle of causality in relation to the subjective-objective discrimination. What can we say in relation to the temporal-eternal distinction? If we postulate an eternal world, characterized by non-successiveness of apprehension, the causal concept as understood in the scientific field cannot be carried over unaltered. Exactly how the phenomenal world as a whole is to be thought of as 'caused' is not for science to determine. Metaphysical questions are deliberately eschewed by natural science. To trace such phenomena ultimately to the activity of Creative Mind is the theological extension of the analogy of human causation. Classical theology has developed this line of thought; and it has its own justification as a process of reasoning—with which, however, we are not concerned here. All that we need to insist on is the essential difference between the eternal and temporal perspectives. We must not make them mutually contradictory. The same physical phenomena are apprehended successively in the temporal and non-successively in the eternal perspective. From the temporal stand-point they follow the laws of science, which are descriptive general statements embodying the principle of causality. From the eternal stand-point these same phenomena presumably have a logic of their own, hidden from our eyes.

Thus, without denying either scientific knowledge or the inscrutability of divine initiative, we insist simply that the temporal and eternal views of the same phenomena are mutually consistent of necessity. We describe the sequence of events in temporal terms, relating each to its phenomenal cause: no other course is open to us. From the vantage-point of eternity God apprehends the whole time-sequence, or space-time representation, in simultaneity. Our knowledge of phenomena is temporal in its essential structure. Consequently such prediction as is possible to us is fore-knowledge in the sense of reasonable expectation, based on previous experience of the same character. God's knowledge of phenomena is neither fore-knowledge nor after-knowledge, strictly speaking. It is complete knowledge, full understanding, with no temporal characteristic whatever. We think in terms of causality, temporally conceived as involving before and after. What 'causality' means from the point of view of eternity we can hardly expect to know. It is sufficient to believe that it implies purposeful creation, and purposeful control appropriate to each level in the created order.

FREEDOM AND THE ETERNAL PERSPECTIVE

Among philosophers the debate between libertarian and determinist views of personal behaviour still continues. There seems little hope that an agreed solution will emerge: human personality is somewhat resistant to intellectual rationalization. A logical dilemma is embedded as it were in the problem; for are we not asking that a man shall fully understand his *own* inmost functioning? The thinking mind is necessarily one stage further behind the particular mental or cerebral process that it seeks to rationalize. At any given stage, if choice is not the result of causes of some kind, rationalization even thus far is an impossibility. If causality operates rigidly, it is not easy to resist a doctrine of complete determinism, which renders all choice illusory. In general the Christian will tend to adhere to a libertarian account of human personality, since his basic experience is one of deliverance from a state of self-bondage. Yet there is freedom and freedom: the natural freedom, which is constantly misused, and leads to a species of slavery; and the supernatural freedom, which comes of accepting the lordship of Christ. But having taken a stand on the reality of free-will and on human responsibility for behaviour, the Christian must at least face a number of problems honestly, even if he cannot solve them to his full intellectual satisfaction. Three such problems are outstanding:

(1) There is indisputable evidence that the freedom of the individual is limited in a variety of ways by physiological or biochemical processes outside his control. Under this heading must be included not only the strange facts known to brain surgery, but also the operation of glands, the effects of drugs, and the diabolical techniques said to be employed in 'brain-washing' in order to extract confessions.

(2) How does it come about that a sequence of events of a physiological and electrical character in the central nervous system can be treated as causally determined; whereas the individual has a sense that he chooses and acts freely? Is this merely the difference between an objective and a subjective view of the same phenomena? And if so, who has the last word? Who has the right to judge whether an act is free?

(3) The Christian doctrine of God has consistently held that omniscience is to be numbered among the divine attributes; and this has been taken to include fore-knowledge not only of natural events but of human actions. How is the freedom of the human will to be reconciled with belief in divine fore-knowledge? Attempts to resolve this paradox by suggesting that choice is not uncaused even though it is free, and that omniscience can 'see its way' through the causal sequences, are far from convincing. If Laplace's omniscient calculator is clean-bowled by physical indeterminacy, he is hardly likely to fare better on the sticky wicket of human mental activity.

In view of the complexity of the issues, it would be foolish to imagine that any simple solution is within our grasp. Some light can be thrown on the matter, however, by following up the distinction between the person himself as a centre of consciousness, and his material embodiment as an intimately related part of the physical order. We shall not fall into the error of treating a human being as 'a ghost inhabiting a machine'. Ryle has (I think) disposed of that bogy by his parable of the steam engine with a ghost-horse inside.[1] A human person is an integral whole. If we talk of body and mind, we are making not a separation of being but a distinction of function. Conscious life is an embodied existence; but judged from the point of view of personal experience it cannot be accounted for exhaustively in material terms. To say that it is 'matter come to consciousness' is only part of the story. Yet it is matter, subject to the laws of matter, which so comes to consciousness. The material embodiment of that 'higher level of being'[2] which we call 'mind' provides the means whereby conscious life draws the greater part of its experience, and shares to a greater or less extent in the materiality of its environment.

In respect of his conscious life, man is in contact with the material order through his five senses, and more subtly through the behaviour of that part of the material world which comprises his bodily organism. His experience is integral to his bodily condition, and includes three diverse but doubtless related elements: (a) apprehension of events wholly external to himself; (b) feelings which he connects with the several parts of his body; and (c) states of feeling, not directly the result of sense perception, and not directly susceptible to analysis by the person concerned. Of these the first group provides the channel of objective knowledge of the environment; the word 'objective' being justified because such knowledge is shared consistently with other persons. The second group of apprehensions is experienced subjectively. It cannot be shared publicly, though it can be identified objectively by the experiencing subject. (The pain is *here*; in my leg.) The third group is essentially subjective, unidentifiable in location, incapable of being shared except sympathetically. (I feel depressed. To which my companion can only reply: I am sorry; I know what you mean: cheer up old boy!) Included in this third group of course is the

---

[1] Gilbert Ryle, in *The Physical Basis of Mind*, ed. Laslett, 75–79. We can accept this point without necessarily endorsing the whole of Ryle's position. N.B.: This author is by no means a materialist as is sometimes thought. 'Man need not be degraded to a machine by being deemed to be a ghost in a machine.' (*The Concept of Mind*, 328.)

[2] The concept goes back to W. Temple (see *Mens Creatrix*, and *Christus Veritas*, 3–5) and has been usefully employed by L. S. Thornton (*The Incarnate Lord*, *passim*).

M

sense of time, already characterized as the subjective experience of entropy change within the bodily organism; and this acts as a kind of fiduciary system for the whole range of conscious experience. Transferred to the clock, the time-sense provides a temporal reference for each item comprised in the three groups above. (Typically: The blizzard began at eight o'clock last evening. The pain came on just before midnight. I feel depressed this morning.) Although time is not strictly a property either of the external world or of the bodily organism, through the unity of self-conscious life all apprehensions (whether objective or purely subjective) are co-ordinated consistently with the sub-jective temporality of the individual. We impose a time-scale on our experience in its wholeness. This is one stage, perhaps the most fundamental, in the comprehension of the environ-ment and the self.

In somewhat the same way we impose the concept of causality upon our environment: for the isolation of phenomenal causes and the recognition of their sequence is possible to us only because external events have been located already in a time-scale. That which can be studied scientifically by a particular self is limited, more or less, to external events; his subjective experience being very largely excluded from such analysis. Nevertheless, the bodily organisms of other selves form part of his external world, and consequently are available to him for scientific study—at least up to a point. More precisely, I can investigate my own class (a), your class (b), but your class (c) hardly at all. Physiology, biochemistry, and neurology are among the fruits of the possible investigations of other selves. And so, provided I overcome my residual solipsism, there is available to me (indirectly) a working objective knowledge of my own bodily organism; in terms of which I can talk airily about what is going on inside my own cerebral cortex.

All this is very obvious; but it needs to be stated, because we too easily gloss over the distinction between the self and the environment: particularly when discussing the functioning of the central nervous system. We can now return to the three outstanding problems which the Christian must face, if he is to take his stand on the reality of free-will.

(1) It is said that the freedom of the individual is limited by physiological or biochemical processes outside his control.

Clearly this is not a matter of looking inside a man's head, while he is deciding something, in order to see how he does it. Indeed this is not an assertion about the normal functioning of conscious personality at all. What we are being told is what happens to freedom when personality is interfered with; or when something mal-functions. To say that 'freedom is limited by . . .' is to admit freedom as the normal condition, and to specify what disturbs it. If another personality is treated as part of the external world, experimented upon (with or without his consent), interfered with; to a degree he ceases to be his own master; his freedom becomes less than it normally is. Thereby objective information of a certain kind is obtained. And such knowledge may be used to treat mental disorders; or, in the wrong hands, to torture and destroy personality.

Now however we react emotionally to such knowledge, the facts must be accepted as part of the objective view of the material order to which scientific study leads us. Although it concerns persons, this is 'it-knowledge'; for in obtaining it we have treated persons as things. We may presume that the same limitations to freedom apply in our own case also: though in the nature of things we have no direct knowledge of our own cerebral functioning. My claim to it-knowledge of myself is distinctly queer. If I make the claim, I do so only half-heartedly; for the sense of freedom remains. Even though I accept that my freedom is sometimes more limited than conscious introspection leads me to suppose, I still do not know when to discount my innate sense of freedom and when to trust it. It-knowledge of myself is particularly useless (in the way that a distorting mirror is useless) yet I cannot deny its deliverances in their proper context. In actual fact we have adjusted ourselves to this new kind of knowledge, as we adjust ourselves to other queer products of the human mind. That is to say, we find we can live with it; for each one of us continues to behave as a sovereign agent. Only our attitude to other selves is at all radically affected. We have become more ready to admit extenuating circumstances: but no less ready to praise. We have learned that we can maintain personal responsibility in general, only if we recognize diminished responsibility in particular cases.

(2) How does it come about that two apparently contradictory accounts of decision-making can be given, one in terms of

causal sequences in the central nervous system, the other in terms of conscious free choice? We are dealing now with the normal functioning of human personality, and in particular with the relation of mind to brain. We need to be especially cautious: first, because mind and brain are not separable entities but distinctions of function; second, because our neuro-physiological knowledge is by no means complete. Hence we have a double duty: to be true to what is known in both fields, mental and neuro-physiological; and not to build a case on the *lacunae* in our knowledge, for this is to invite subsequent falsification. Science can give us a reasonably full account of perception, and the mechanisms by which *stimuli* from the external world are conveyed to the appropriate regions in the cortex. It can also give a reasonably full account of motor action, both voluntary and involuntary: that is to say, it can explain in causal terms how certain electrical changes in the cortex lead to muscular movements. But at present a large question-mark stands between these two accounts. There is a vital gap in our knowledge; and it is in this gap that we are tempted to locate the brain-mind distinction. Having received information through the sensory nerves, how does the brain arrive at a decision and send out appropriate impulses through the motor nerves? Is this even the right question to ask? If we are to preserve the correct logical and linguistic conventions, we can speak of the brain receiving and sending out impulses (for 'brain' and 'impulse' belong to the same world); and we can speak of the mind receiving information and making decisions (for this is its particular function). To confuse the two languages gets us nowhere.

The neuro-physiological picture is incomplete. Indeed it lets us down precisely at the point where accurate information is most to be desired. To substitute speculation for scientific knowledge is dangerous. We can usefully notice, however, the two possible ways in which the gap might be bridged. Either we think of the mind as something which de-codes information, comes to a decision, and issues its commands in code to the brain; or by an act of faith we presume that causally-determined processes, as yet unknown, bridge the gap in its entirety. The former alternative separates mind and brain, where we should do no more than record a functional distinction: it puts back the ghost, previously exorcised, into the machine. This is not the way out of our difficulties. The latter alternative preserves the unity of the neuro-physiological picture, avoiding obscurantism and unnecessary mystification; but it appears to deal a death-blow to the autonomy of personal life, unless we add the proviso that it is simply one of two parallel stories, the other being in mental terms. In other words, if we are to be true to what is known in both fields, mental and neuro-physiological, we must be content to employ two languages side by side. We must describe the brain-mind complex objectively in terms of neuro-physiology with its appropriate causal sequences, and subjectively in terms of the conscious experience of knowing and deciding. In this manner only do we avoid a disastrous dualism; so preserving the given unity of being with distinction of function.

This view of the matter, however, has been seriously criticised. Austin Farrer[1] takes the line that 'personal-life language and neuro-physiological language about the human body' are not legitimate parallel ways of talking about the matter, one from inside, one from outside. So far from the problem being exploded, it is simply glossed over, he suggests; for the relation of mind to brain is unique: no adequate analogy can be found elsewhere to justify the use of parallel languages. He therefore insists that there must be 'a *tertium quid*, a large-scale pattern of physical action directly correlative with consciousness at certain points, and productive of real physical effects. And the postulation of such a principle is no mere evasion of an unwelcome or even of an untenable alternative. It is the giving of full value to the only clue we have for the relation between mental activity and bodily performance—the case where what I mentally enact I physically perform.'[2] In Farrer's opinion, to place personal-life language and neuro-physiological language in simple parallel leads to epiphenomenalism, i.e. to a view in which mind arises from the complex behaviour of matter on the large scale, but which denies to mind any corresponding effect on matter. The objection has force; but is not, I think, conclusive.

Our knowledge of mental and neuro-physiological activity is not only incomplete: it is essentially empirical. What right have

[1] Austin Farrer, *The Freedom of the Will*, 64 f.   [2] *loc. cit.*, 80.

we to expect that we can integrate two such different fields of empirical experience into one tidy system? The materialist will produce tidiness at the expense of mind: the idealist at the expense of matter. An honestly empirical approach will admit that two lines of investigation, *each valid in its own sphere*, lead to two descriptions of personal activity. For some purposes we must use one language, for others the alternative (rather as atomic physics uses the complementary languages of particles and waves). Since the mind-brain relationship is unique, the empirical approach need not distress us. Indeed there is good reason for insisting simply on the *equal validity* of the two languages (personal and neuro-physiological) as empirical fact. In this way we safeguard what we know, without pretending to what we do not know. The objective view, arrived at by scientific investigation and assuming no gap in the causal process applies primarily to other selves. It is 'it-knowledge'. The subjective view, arrived at by introspection and the analysis of conscious experience, applies primarily to the self. It is 'I-knowledge'. The two languages belong to distinct perspectives of the same conscious self.[1]

For the external perspective, events are causally determined; and this means no more than that we recognize sequences of connected phenomena, such that A is uniformly antecedent to B in a time-scale based on our subjective sense of temporality. But is this a complete explanation of events external to ourselves? Not at all. It is a partial rationalization, achieved by

[1] In taking personal-life language and neuro-physiological language to be complementary in Bohr's sense (cf. waves and particles), we must be satisfied that there is no *logical* contradiction between them. Now here the two stories are descriptive in character, each having its own internal consistency. One story is about nerves, cells, electrical impulses, and the like; the other about persons, and purposeful activity. *Can* there be logical contradiction between two descriptive statements which to all intents are about different items? No overlapping of content implies the corollary, no logical contradiction. Thus, I would suggest that the difference of language is purely *formal*, corresponding to description of what is apprehended from alternative, and mutually exclusive, stand-points (internal and external). Neither, presumably, contains the whole truth: both are concessions to the frailty of human thinking. Consequently we are free to conceive the facts themselves (as known *sub specie aeternitatis*) as analogous to a three-dimensional reality, apprehended as one or other of alternative two-dimensional projections— just as a circle and a rectangle are alternative projections in two dimensions of what in three dimensions is a right circular cylinder. Formal difference without logical contradiction is of the essence of truly complementary descriptions of a more complex reality; and that I suggest is the case here.

pressing the analogy of the self as personal cause. I can cause certain events in my external world: therefore events of which I am not the cause can be rationalized analogically by the supposition of some other causal agency. Where animism postulated a world of spirit agencies, modern science recognizes uniform antecedent phenomenal causation.

Nevertheless, this picture of external reality is fabricated by a sovereign self. It stands or falls with the autonomy of the self.

My own sense of freedom as a sovereign agent, and therefore my ability to be the cause of anything, is integral to personal experience. Indeed it is the logical starting-point of any rational account of the external world. The sovereign freedom of the self is implicit in the scientific outlook: it cannot seriously be doubted. Even though for public purposes I entertain the external objective view of science, and discuss its details as (presumably) they concern my own mental functioning, my sovereign freedom remains unquestioned. The libertarian view of human activity is the knower's knowledge of himself. The determinist view is the observer's rational picture of someone else: thought of (rather unfairly, it must be conceded) as an 'it' in the world outside. The determinist view returns, boomerang fashion, to deal a fatal blow to my own knowledge of myself only when I fail to recognize the true status of the account which I give of my external world.

Choosing or deciding is a mysterious business. Let us admit it. I can give reasons which have weighed with me in coming to a decision, but not causes which have compelled me. 'Reasons' belong to the mental language: 'causes' to the alternative neuro-physiological language.[1] We must not confuse them. The reasons are arguments which I take into consideration; one of which I allow to determine my choice. But this is not the determinism of natural science. Decision is determined (in the basic personal sense of the word) by the sovereign agent whose decision it is. And we cannot go behind that mysterious fact of our human existence.

(3) How is the freedom of the human will to be reconciled with belief in the omniscience of God? The common-sense view, which finds contradiction here, is fallacious because it fails to

1 See P. Alexander, *Rational Behaviour and Psycho-analytic Explanation*, In *Mind*, 71, 326–41 (1962).

recognize the difference between the temporal and the eternal modes of apprehension. Just as I impose my own time-scale upon the external world, so here the common-sense view of divine omniscience mistakenly imposes a time-scale upon the eternal world. The one is a permissible step towards the rationalization of our experience of the material environment: the other involves an illegitimate distortion of reality. The external world is subject to change; and to impose time upon it is to offer an interpretation which is generally congruous; since the time-sense is the subjective experience of change. The eternal world, however, is not subject to change. To impose time upon it, as a step towards interpretation, is not in any sense congruous. Indeed, any attempt to deal with the eternal mode of apprehension in temporal terms is utterly fallacious. In particular, it leads immediately to the apparent contradiction between divine omniscience and human free-will. No progress in understanding is possible unless we recognize the simultaneity of non-temporal apprehension, and make due allowance for this mode in our specification of divine omniscience. Then, as in the former problem, we have to deal with a difference of perspective. Each perspective is fully valid in its own sphere: neither must be carried over unaltered into the opposite mode of apprehension.

I can give an account of my own activity in temporal terms, accepting responsibility for my behaviour, and insisting on my sovereign freedom within my own sphere. Such an account is my immediate, inalienable, knowledge of my own conscious life. I am told that my freedom can be reduced by the malfunctioning of my glands or the administration of drugs—and I firmly believe it! What I cannot admit, without logical inconsistency, is that what I suppose to be my choice is always determined by phenomenal causes; though I readily agree that the rationalization of cerebral activity from the angle of an external observer involves the causal mode of description. That is to say, the manner in which a person interprets his external world necessitates a perspective inappropriate to the understanding of his own conscious life as experienced. Since therefore personal choice is normally both free and responsible, no person existing temporally can know in advance how I shall choose or act. He can guess, but he cannot know. *Even I* do not know how I shall choose. If I did know, I should already have chosen. The impossibility of fore-knowledge of personal decision is implicit in temporality. This logic is falsely exhibited, however, when it is supposed to lead to a contradiction between human freedom and divine omniscience. The logic is sound enough: but only in its right place, i.e. under conditions of strict temporality.

I can remotely conceive that from the stand-point of eternity my choices and actions take on a 'new look'. The entire train of decisions, which constitutes my active mental existence, is apprehended in a non-temporal mode by a being who inhabits the eternal world. The non-temporal mode of apprehension, characterized by simultaneity, stands in complete contrast to the temporal mode, characterized by successiveness. A train of events, physical or mental, which occupies a span of time in the temporal order, is apprehended as a unity in the eternal 'now'. This essentially different perspective of necessity permits a fuller knowledge. Christian talk of divine fore-knowledge is intended to safeguard this fulness; but logically considered the choice of terms is unfortunate.

To say that God knows how I shall choose *before* I choose is meaningless, strictly speaking; for God is not in time. To talk in this way is to transport temporal modes of knowing (the implications of the word 'before') into the eternal world where they are inappropriate. It is equally illegitimate to say that God knows how I choose *after* I have chosen: and for the same reason—'after' is a temporal word. 'Before' and 'after' are meaningful only in terms of a time-series. They describe experiences which are not shared by eternal being. The truth is that the entire succession of choices, which constitutes my conscious life, is apprehended and known in complete simultaneity by God. From the stand-point of eternity my temporal sequence of choices, like the sequence of my external acts, is known somewhat as the frames of an unrolled cine-film can be known: all together, in their completeness as a sequence. But this does not detract from the logic of free choices, made successively under temporal conditions. We have been given the power of initiation under conditions of temporality. This is the inner mystery of personality, by which we share remotely in the function of divinity.

It is clear then that we must postulate the completeness of God's knowledge of our choices, not because of his infinity but on account of his timelessness. We can do so without compromising the reality of our own derivative yet sovereign freedom, within the limits imposed by the material constitution of our bodily organisms. Since God apprehends all events and all decisions in the eternal mode, there is no instant of *time* at which his knowledge is not complete. If in this sense he is said to have fore-knowledge, the 'knowledge' belongs to the eternal order, and is peculiar to it, while the 'fore' belongs to the temporal order. But should we be guilty of joining our 'fore' to God's 'knowledge'? This is a logical impropriety indeed, even for religious language!

XII

REVELATION OF THE ETERNAL

THE newer attitude to revelation, hailed as a return to the
biblical view, means that we no longer conceive divine truth as
imparted to us by some mysterious process in propositional
form, so that the very words are sacrosanct. We recognize
rather that God's revelation of himself is given historically
through events which range widely in character. The Exodus
from Egypt is revelatory, the Life of Christ supremely so: and
between poles as diverse as these must be included the principal
turning points of Hebrew history; indeed in a sense every detail
of the historical process, sacred or secular.

No historical occurrence, however, can reveal God unless
human insight is enabled to grasp its meaning. Fact and
interpretation are equally necessary if revelation is to take place.
The use of the word 'history' commonly fails to distinguish
these two elements. Sometimes the reference is to a mere
chronicle of events; and where this attitude prevails, the
scientific approach is held to require only the accurate reporting
of what occurred. A more mature view, observing that even
the selection of events for reporting implies a recognition of
relative significance, insists that no history worthy of the name,
not even secular history, can be blind to the interpretation of
what is recorded. If, therefore, we say that the historical process
is the medium of revelation, we mean that God is known
through his historical activity together with a valid understanding of that activity. This is indeed the biblical view. To
which we can only add that the inspired understanding of
history is by no means universal: everything depends on the
culture to which a man belongs. Revelation in the first instance
was to a particular people; and later through them to the world
at large. Only within a particular ethnic group was there

found the spiritual response which discerned the divine initiative. If therefore history is the arena of God's activity, the particularity of human response implies the particularity of divine purpose. Historical events, an understanding of their significance, and a continuing community which sees itself as the People of God—these are the three legs on which revelation stands. Knock out any one, and the biblical position becomes insupportable.

Now while all this is commonplace in the context of modern biblical studies, it raises two questions of special interest for the somewhat larger view which is our present concern. *First,* How are we justified in claiming that the historical process falls under the general control of the divine? Manifestly, apart from such control, at least in the sense of an over-ruling providence, the concept of revelation through historical events would be without foundation. But *second*, and this is every bit as important, What possibility is there of real contact between Divine Mind and finite human minds, on the basis of which we may claim that the significance of events is discerned as revelation? These questions taken together clearly cover both the historical existence and the spiritual functioning of the community through which revelation takes place: a culture in which fact is met by faith, and significance by perception. These matters, touched on in previous chapters, must now be examined in the light of the relationship between time and eternity; and our conception of this relation should enable us to penetrate more deeply into the meaning of revelation and the manner of its operation as a fact of religious history.

THE HISTORICAL PROCESS

Whether the emphasis in history is placed upon events themselves or upon their interpretation in broader terms, the rational mind is not content with a mere succession of unconnected occurrences. Both common sense and professional training dispose the historian to search for reasons if not for causes, for motivation if not for determinism; and though human affairs are incomparably more complex in character than the processes of inanimate nature, scientific ideals demand nevertheless that events of history be related in some sense to their antecedent conditions. That is to say, while motives and reasons arise in the human mind, and in turn sway the activities of human populations, they are seldom unrelated either to the material conditions of life or to events which have already taken place. The unravelling of this complex in geographical, economic, psychological, or ideological terms is the equivalent for the historian of exhibiting the facts as a causal sequence: if not in the sense of a sequence absolutely determined by inexorable laws, at least in the sense of a reasonable explanation of why men acted as they did. Though such a patterning leaves large questions unanswered, tending in particular to pass over the influence of outstanding personalities, it has become the convention to locate the causes of historical events in the tangible factors of geography and economics, and in the less tangible concepts of the spirit of a people or a world movement. And, it must be admitted, up to a point such an approach has proved its usefulness.

Even before the establishment of states and empires, terrain and climate impose their influences on a people; since in a purely physical manner they determine the possible ways of life and agriculture, limiting the size of a population in relation to available resources and technical competence. Natural boundaries too, in the shape of sea, river, or mountain range, cannot fail to influence the corporate sense of a people and consequently to condition its history. The obvious example of the situation of ancient Israel in the Fertile Crescent is constantly quoted in relation to the economy and the vulnerability of the Hebrew people. Arising in some degree from geography and economics, the pressure exerted by a virile population, or the relative vacuum presented by a sparse one, accounts in some measure for the ambition and the ability to engage in conquest. Yet it is clear that something more than population statistics is involved here. We commonly refer to the 'spirit of a people'—a phrase of wide generality, held to include such opposing factors as ferocity and servility, moral health and decadence, freshness and lassitude. Even the secular approach cannot fail to recognize the existence of factors other than the purely material. And what of that intangible something referred to as the 'spirit of the times'? At particular periods certain ideas, certain mass movements and incentives, appear to dominate the historical process: nationalism, colonialism, and a host of others with the same ending. Always ill-defined, these factors are invoked invariably when the march of events cannot be otherwise accounted for. Irresistible forces, near deterministic in their operation, often irrational in themselves, are held to underlie the tendency for similar developments under diverse physical conditions at much the same epoch. So far from being explanations in any logical sense, such factors serve rather to hold together conceptually wide ranges of essentially similar happenings: their power is descriptive and evocative rather than causal.

Now in a very general way we are at liberty to point to the 'hand of God' in each of these ingredients of conventional historical explanation. Geography, we may say, is what it is in virtue of the operation of large-scale laws of nature, which in turn express the mind of the Creator. The moral fibre of a nation is connected with its response, individual and corporate, to the ethical law implanted in the human heart. Ideas and ideals, even ideologies, which activate whole peoples, represent either the response of mankind to spiritual values, or their rejection. While there is truth in all this, by itself it makes a somewhat flimsy foundation for any doctrine of the divine control of history. More important, it fails to meet the critical outlook of historians on their own ground. If there is a more profound lesson to be learned from the study of the past, it is that these identifiable factors by themselves do not account fully for the historical process. Isaiah Berlin,[1] in a penetrating polemic, criticizes the attitude to history which makes it the inevitable outcome of the operation of 'vast impersonal forces', pouring scorn on the view that 'to be wise is to understand the direction in which the world is inexorably moving, to identify oneself with the rising power which ushers in the new world'. He insists that the various promises 'to assimilate the human sciences to the natural in the quest for a unified schema of all there is . . . have conspicuously failed to keep their word'. Which is only sober truth.

If historical determinism is to be rejected, it follows that undue attention need not be given to the relating of supernatural control with the existence of large-scale laws of wide

[1] Isaiah Berlin, *Historical Inevitability*, 23, 76.

generality. Theological interpretation must base itself more firmly. Where then do we look for the rock which can serve as a foundation? Two observations must be made. (1) Theological interpretation should be empirically based: that is to say, it must stand upon *discrete* facts of history such as may be universally recognized by the unprejudiced. It should offer an explanation of these facts; which, though it may command acceptance only from those who are theologically committed, at least grows out of them, rather than is artificially forced upon them in a denominational interest. And the facts of which we must take account are often those which the discredited determinist approach has either glossed over or not deigned to notice: particular, significant, unpredictable occurrences; and those outstanding personalities whose influence on the future course of history is an embarrassment to any tidy theory. (2) Then again, theological interpretation should fasten on to that aspect of empirical happening which is its own proper concern: namely the rightness or wrongness of motive or action. It must not fear to judge; and having judged, to follow up the implications of its view of events, notwithstanding the charge of partisanship from certain quarters. A colourless neutrality, even scientifically inspired, can never carry the weight of theological interpretation: a full-blooded judgement, which is not afraid to praise or to condemn, in spite of the moral vulnerability of the one who so discriminates, is the only possible basis of the doctrine that the Righteous God is Lord of History. Berlin,[1] though he might reject such specific interpretation himself, is our ally at least to the extent that he emphasizes the historian's obligation to pass moral judgements on the characters and events of the past. Moral judgement is the *sine qua non* of any theological interpretation worthy of the name.

The peculiar importance of apparently insignificant events, which seem to 'trigger off' a chain of happenings, has of course been noted by a number of writers. It has been suggested, plausibly as it may appear to the uncommitted, that we should recognize the casual as well as the causal element in history. 'The historian is wise if, like the Romans of the early Empire, he admits Fortuna and even Sors to a place in his Pantheon, and concedes the eternal presence of the irrational and the

1 *loc. cit.*, 76 f.

inexplicable'. So writes Buchan,[1] proceeding then to give an illustration from recent history: 'The success of Turkish Nationalism under Kemal was due to the complete rout of the Greek armies in 1922 in Asia Minor. That ill-omened Greek campaign was largely due to the restoration in 1920 of King Constantine... King Constantine was recalled as a consequence of a general election . . . and that election was held because young King Alexander . . . died early in the autumn of 1920. The cause of his death was blood-poisoning due to the bite of a pet monkey in the palace gardens. I cannot better Mr. Churchill's comment: "A quarter of a million persons died of that monkey's bite".' Both the temper of the comment, and the substance of the illustration, are far removed from theological interpretation. The recognition of such trains of events at the secular level, however, by writers who have no theological axe to grind, provides an insight into the stuff of real history which is altogether lacking in the determinist view. But is this a legitimate writing of history?

Of course it is easy to overpress the argument from particularity; and thoroughly fallacious to ignore those other causal influences which make their contribution to the eventual outcome, just in order to draw attention to one striking but apparently random element in the sequence of events. Richardson[2] has protested strongly against this method of twisting the presentation of the past: his criticism is all the more apposite when it is turned against the imbecile attempt to drag in the 'Finger of God' prematurely as the explanation of the particular, unpredictable, occurrence which is held to have had such enormous consequences.

The writing of history must place the particular and the significant against the background of the causal. The uniquely significant is the unexplained element: what follows reveals the logic of the historical process, where explanation is not out of place. It is on the unique happenings that we must fasten our attention if we are to offer an interpretation; for these are the guiding lights by which we get our bearings, the cairns that mark the way through the mist to the summit. *Post eventum* a national culture commonly does fasten onto the unique events

[1] J. Buchan, *Men and Deeds*, 8 f.
[2] Alan Richardson, *History, Sacred and Profane*, 98 f.

in its own history, offering an interpretation (where no explanation is forthcoming) in terms of its own particular outlook. Such interpretation may or may not be valid—who is to say?—but that is not yet the point at issue. We recognize simply that these events of a unique character are necessarily the points at which human interpretation, whether nationalistic or religious, is active. Exceptional phenomena of nature (the crossing of the Red Sea or the storm which destroyed the Armada), the sudden appearance of an energetic leader capable of inspiring multitudes: these are the happenings which the minds of men insist on appropriating to themselves as evidence of some sort of benevolence in the mysterious powers which lie behind the march of events.

Granted that men insist on finding interpretations for the great turning points of their history, there is no limit to the kind of pattern they may discern. To a large extent the recognition of pattern in history is subjective: it is not thereby rendered illusory. Among the subjective interpretations some are valid, others not. And just here lies the difficulty of any writing of history which is more than a chronicle of events. What one man discerns clearly to his own satisfaction, another rejects as altogether unfounded. Even Toynbee's magisterial *Study of History*, with its stress on withdrawal, opportunity, and response, leading to universal empires, and later to universal Churches, plausible though it seems to some is flatly rejected by others. Nothing could illustrate more clearly the importance of the subjective element which man brings to his task when he embarks on a course of historical interpretation. For this reason it will be suggested, and rightly, that the Christian pattern of interpretation is discernible only to those who stand within the Christian tradition and share its outlook. Again however this does not make the interpretation illusory. It merely underlines its presuppositions: and no history-writing is without presuppositions.

If the theological interpretation of history is to justify itself, it must make plain its prior assumptions, and indicate the historical criteria which it seeks to apply, commending its approach as a whole to the mind and conscience of mankind. While responsible theological interpretation will certainly fasten onto the particular, it will not pick on what is trivial. Nor will it distort the record by ignoring the larger causal

N

factors or motives whose influence proves decisive in the long run. Nor yet will it afford itself the distinction, basic to the position taken up by such as Buchan, between the casual and the casual. The Christian theologian does not have a Pantheon. He can have no truck with Fortuna, still less with Sors. Denying that the unpredictable is necessarily 'casual', and insisting on the personal as well as the phenomenal connotation of 'causal', his monotheism leads him to recognize a divine guidance of the historical process as a whole. But he admits, or rather he stresses, that this discernment is possible only when persons and their historical actions are submitted to the moral judgement. An interpretation which is not based upon the discrimination of right and wrong by an informed conscience is worse than subjective: it is self-stultifying.

The Christian interpretation of history has its roots in Old Testament soil. The consciousness that God is Lord of history can be traced back to the earliest traditions of the Exodus. Whatever the actual facts may have been, here is a significant occurrence, unique, unexpected, unrepeatable, whose long-term consequences were to be enormous. From this event, perhaps more even than from patriarchal legends, stems the consciousness of Israel as the Chosen People: an optimistic interpretation-pattern which future events would have to deepen. There is no need to tell the story of this deepening. It is sufficient to recall that prophetic denunciations of other nations on moral grounds led logically to similar charges against Israel, whose lapses were the more serious in proportion to her greater privilege; that if Israel deserved the judgement of God, her calamities must be identified with God's disciplining of his people; that if only a remnant remained, the future fulfilment of God's purpose rested, humanly speaking, on that purified remnant; that even the sufferings of a righteous minority, either with or at the hands of an unrighteous nation, could be mysteriously redemptive: in short, that revelation calls for, and calls forth, obedience and commitment. These well-known prophetic teachings form a logically-developing interpretation of history, never indeed put together as a single thesis, but as the Old Testament literature takes shape profoundly deepening the optimism from which the tradition began. Here in the making are the moral judgements fundamental to the Christian interpretation of history. As Epstein[1] puts it, the prophets were 'the conscience of their generation'.

Butterfield,[2] examining this Old Testament interpretation from the angle of the professional historian, finds in it much that is permanently valid as a 'mundane comment on human affairs and on the moral problems involved', quite apart from the question of the truth of the supernatural religion in terms of which it is formulated. 'What was unique about the ancient Hebrews was their historiography rather than their history—the fact that their finer spirits saw the hand of God in events, ultimately realizing that if they were the Chosen People they were chosen for the purpose of transmitting that discovery to all other nations.'[3] The transformation of the sense of privilege to include the sense of painful vocation was the most profound moulding of a people by its religion which the world has witnessed. But without some share in the experience there can be no full grasp or acceptance of the outlook which was created by that experience. Thus it is that the Judeo-Christian interpretation commends itself primarily to those who are the spiritual heirs of this living religious tradition. Acceptance or rejection of the interpretation is connected ultimately with acceptance or rejection of the gospel. As Butterfield[4] puts it, 'I am unable to see how a man can find the hand of God in secular history, unless he has first found that he has an assurance of it in his personal experience. . . . In this sense our interpretation of the human drama throughout the ages rests finally on our interpretation of our most private experience of life, and stands as merely an extension of it.'

It is relatively easy to pass moral judgements, particularly if we allow ourselves to adopt a position of detachment. But does the historical process endorse our judgements? Theological interpretation, we said, must be empirically based. How many tyrants have come to a sticky end? How many righteous men have suffered at their hands? How do we strike a balance between them? We cannot: for these things do not add up. We may set Macbeth against Duncan; Ahab against Naboth. What can we set against Jesus of Nazareth? The two thieves dying for their misdeeds do not 'balance' the One Righteous

[1] Isidore Epstein, *Judaism*, 55.   [2] H. Butterfield, *Christianity and History*, 24.
[3] *loc. cit.*, 73.   [4] *loc. cit.*, 107.

Man who hung between them: nor would a thousand thieves. The Christian interpretation of history is the conviction held, often in the face of odds, by the man of faith. It cannot be proved: nor can it be disproved. The Christian claim to find meaning in history expresses the faith which has come to terms with the Cross—its challenge, its seeming defeat, and its victory. Indeed the Cross is the one key that unlocks the door of mystery; imparting deep seriousness and responsibility to our interpretation of the historical process. For, reduced to its barest elements, what does history tell us? That men sinned, and suffered, and died; but that among the millions who have lived, One stands apart who was without sin, who died as no other man has died. Here is moral judgement at work, assessing the facts of history. Christians believe that he rose from the dead and lives eternally. Here is both history,[1] and the declaration of faith which gives meaning to history.

Theological interpretation and acceptance of the Christian faith go together. They are mutually supporting. The man who stands outside the Christian tradition, regarding commitment as prejudice, demands what he calls scientific neutrality. But what is this so-called scientific neutrality? In the affairs of men there is no such thing. Since it is impossible to write history without presuppositions of some kind, it is better that presuppositions should be examined and admitted than that their existence should be overlooked. The only alternative to Christian commitment is the rejection of the gospel as untrue, or at best irrelevant. No neutrality is conceivable; and the adjective 'scientific' in this connection is little more than a piece of bluff.[2] In the final analysis, the justification of the Christian interpretation of history is Augustine's *credo ut intellegam*. We admit it without equivocation.

SUB SPECIE AETERNITATIS

When we affirm that human history is the arena of God's

---

[1] A. Richardson (*History, Sacred and Profane*, 206–212) justifies the claim that the Resurrection is history, though he will commit himself to no historical reconstruction in detail.

[2] The 'scientific' aspect of historical enquiry is the careful examination of evidence, with the object of laying bare the empirical facts. Once interpretation begins, scientific attitudes have no place: human judgement supervenes.

purposeful activity, we speak from faith to faith. That events sometimes appear to belie the theory of divine guidance we readily admit, particularly where the temporal horizon is most limited. Yet it is the universal experience of Christian men that the deepening of faith and the ability to take the longer view go hand in hand; and we may believe with justification that *sub specie aeternitatis* all fits into a purposeful and essentially good pattern of divine guidance. Since, however, we recognize the reality of human freedom, and know not only in others but more especially in ourselves the reality of rebellion, we cannot pretend that all historical occurrence, without exception, is divinely willed. The pattern which faith discerns, that is to say, is a very general one, superposed by omniscience upon a relatively unpatterned complex of human decisions, expressing both co-operation with and opposition to the divine will in the actual detail of events. This is what was implied in chapter X when we spoke of the overall pattern of the world-lines, which in space-time represent the sum total of events in the created order.

In view of the complexity of the issue from the theological stand-point, it is significant that the only faith which discerns a meaningful pattern in history has a very definite place for divine judgement reflected in adversity, as well as for benevolence reflected in prosperity. That is to say, the Christian view of history is not a superficial view, any more than Christianity is a shallow faith. The reading of the Old Testament and the study of the gospel show clearly that this interpretation was achieved only by an interplay of insight with event, which renders untenable earlier (and later) optimistic views. It implies righteousness as well as omnipotence in the divine: indeed the righteousness of omnipotence, and the omnipotence of righteousness. The Christian interpretation of history is essentially a moral view, which takes seriously the rightness or wrongness of every human act.

Having exhibited the grounds on which we hold the Christian view of history, and the degree of personal commitment which it entails, we must now ask how does our concept of the relationship of time to eternity help us to see things in their wholeness. It deepens our understanding of divine omniscience by filling out the artist analogy of the creative act.

The inclusion of fore-knowledge, so called, in divine omniscience can be misleading unless we recognize the distinction between the temporal and the eternal modes of knowing. From the temporal standpoint human freedom is a reality which follows its own logic of reasons and motives. From the eternal perspective the successive moments of temporal existence and activity are known unitively, without that successiveness which gives to the temporal order its peculiar characteristic. Thus, to insist on divine omniscience in its fulness, there is no need to deny either human freedom or human responsibility. Now clearly without omniscience in the fullest sense, the purposive and effectual guidance of history would be impossible. Divine activity in the world would be uncertain of its fulfilment, were it not for the special quality of the eternal mode of knowing. Within more narrow limits human political decisions are the attempt to guide the course of events. But how differently do they operate! How infrequently do they achieve what they intend! More often than not even the wisest of political purposes is defeated by the unexpectedness of events and the stubborn wilfulness of human nature. From the temporal stand-point these things cannot be foreseen except in the most general terms. Even the most sagacious decisions are made perforce with incomplete knowledge. The future course of events shows up the inadequacy of our planning. And this cannot be otherwise. By contrast, divine omniscience sees in its wholeness the complex of events and human decisions which supervene in time. What is known unitively from the eternal perspective appears only successively, as it comes to pass, in the limited temporal perspective. The secret of divine omniscience is the wholeness of the eternal mode of apprehension. Without it only a patchy, stop-go, kind of guidance would be logically possible.

We have thought of God as the Creative Artist. From the point of view of time it seems that the dramatist supplies the most convincing form of the analogy; whereas from the standpoint of eternity we may conceive the art-form as the creation of an intricate pattern, static in a sense, finished and complete in its wholeness, though dynamic as it passes into temporal realization. The one is the analogue of the other; the distinction a matter of perspective. Now it is of the nature of an artist to express himself, in the sense that he puts something of his own being and his own values into his work. Hence we may say that the artistic work of the Creator expresses his own being within the limits imposed by the medium; which in this case is not only chosen but willed. Its limitations are intended; indeed given in the creative act. Thus, the medium with its limitations (human nature active historically) is that which the Creator has brought into being in order to express himself.

The moral character of the Artist-Creator is expressed consequently, within appropriate limits, in the total historical process. It is with no surprise that we find something of the character of God as a moral being built into the structure and significance of events, both on the large scale and on the small; both in the broad sweep of the historical process, and in the more intimate detail of our own daily existence. For this reason alone human experience in history, properly understood, is revelatory. The holiness and righteousness of fatherly love, the reality of answering love and the acceptance of its cost, the fact of judgement and forgiveness, are expressed and revealed in the texture of what the existentialists call 'authentic living'. The Divine Artist declares himself in the maturing of historical process, as in the personal experience accorded to the actors in the drama. One self-consistent revelation is to be seen at both levels. Though specific historical events of outstanding significance, such as deliverance and national judgement, constitute the highlights of divine activity; all events and all sequences, when viewed in sufficiently extended perspective, are revelatory in their degree. But such revelation is clear only where there is commitment. *Credo ut intellegam.* Unless we stand within the particular religious and cultural community, created to be the channel of universal revelation, the faith is not yet open to us by which we even begin to understand.

ETERNAL MIND AND TEMPORAL MINDS

We come now to the other question of more general philosophical interest. How are we to conceive the contact of divine Mind with human minds? If events are to be revelatory, meaning must be discerned in them as well as imparted to them. For history to become the means of communication involves a bridging of the gap between the eternal and the temporal.

In attempting to throw light upon this aspect of revelation, it is well to start from the relationship between minds at the temporal level, of which we know something directly in human experience. Understanding between minds involves a measure of affinity. Like answers like. As we say colloquially, we are 'on the same wave-length'. Now here we have the first necessary condition for communication between Eternal Mind and temporal minds; and we recognize immediately one facet of what is meant by the creation of man in the divine image. Not only have we mental and spiritual faculties, believed to be akin to the divine; we share, though imperfectly, in the same set of values. The righteousness of God is absolute, perfect, and primary: but man has by nature and grace an inherent sense of righteousness, which reflects imperfectly the divine righteousness. Hence the response which God's righteousness finds in the human mind at its best. We recognize it for what it is; it means something to us; which we cannot and need not define further, in that it belongs to our created nature as persons. And what is true here equally is true of other so-called attributes of God.

But there is more to be said. Minds that are akin to one another are capable of mutual understanding. As mutual understanding progresses they become if anything more alike. Even between temporal minds we recognize a kind of mutual indwelling, a measure of interpenetration of mind by mind. Now 'indwelling' and 'interpenetration' are spatial metaphors, and entirely natural ones at that; for in human experience temporal minds are spatially embodied, and in some sense 'carried about' by the persons to whom they belong. The use of spatial metaphors, however, does not commit us to a spatial concept of mind: in a mysterious way even temporal minds transcend their spatial embodiment. The interpenetration of mind by mind is one aspect of their non-localization; as it is the basis of our deepest experience of one another in friendship, love, and communion. We know; and in knowing we are known, under conditions of temporality.

Such interpenetration of minds may be, and most commonly is, between equals; or it may involve the relationship of teacher to disciple, of mature to immature. Clearly the former offers no suitable analogy for the understanding of revelation; whereas the latter does. The interpenetration of the mind of the teacher and the mind of the disciple is a more one-sided relationship than that between equals. The mind of the disciple is 'drawn into' the mind of the teacher by the act of learning: there is a sharing on one side of what is already understood on the other. Between temporal subjects, however, the relationship is never entirely one-sided; for this would imply the complete domination of the disciple by the teacher—a denial both of the full personality of the disciple and of the principles of sound education. At the human level there is always an entry of the mind of the teacher into that of the disciple, as well as an entry of the mind of the disciple into that of the teacher: that is to say true interpenetration. Now here we have a valid and useful analogy for the relationship of Eternal Mind and temporal minds; and the respect and reverence of the teacher for the taught is highly significant as we follow out its implications.

In examining the learning process by which interpenetration takes place between the Mind of God and the mind of man, at least five points should be noted; and each but the last has its proper analogy in the relationship of teacher to taught under human conditions. *First*, there is the ability to recognize the identity of the Teacher: in biblical language, 'to hear the word', or 'to discern the spirits'. *Second*, the readiness to learn: what the prophet Micah speaks of as 'walking humbly with thy God'. *Third*, the ability to trust: the readiness to make single steps in faith, by the light of what has been given already, without asking to see further before committing oneself. *Fourth*, the willingness to worship: and worship is the recognition of the disparity between the Creator and the creature. All these points indicate the prerequisites of any real interpenetration; yet by themselves they do not answer the essential question. *Last* therefore, and most important of all, is the ability to transcend the temporal perspective in some degree; and so to enter, however imperfectly, into an eternal mode of apprehension and knowing.

No knowledge of the divine is conceivable apart from such self-transcendence. The human capacity to enter into the eternal, in a limited degree, is what characterizes our religious life and our participation in spiritual reality. It is the *sine qua non* of theological insight and conceptualization. It was this apprehension of the unchanging element in our deepest experience which led us in the first instance to formulate the idea of eternity, and to distinguish the temporal and the eternal modes of being. Even in the natural sciences the recognition of an unchanging pattern, which we express in the form of laws, is an apprehension of the eternal;[1] possible to us because, while we inhabit the temporal order, we have a limited capacity to transcend the merely temporal. In all this mental activity, secular as well as sacred, we are surely right in recognizing a human learning of what is in the mind of God: a real interpenetration of minds, temporal and eternal.

The prophetic figures of the Old Testament provide the most notable instances of the human mind being drawn into an understanding of things divine. When the prophets describe their experiences as visions, or auditions, the language employed may be no more than a recognition of the fact that communication between human minds is normally through the channels of hearing and sight; or it may represent some real psychological conditioning of apprehension, indistinguishable subjectively from hearing and seeing. What is beyond dispute is that the prophetic consciousness entered into, and in turn was possessed by, the mind of the Eternal; and that in this interpenetration of minds the condition of mere temporality was transcended in a remarkable degree. Interpenetration is the coming together of persons into mutual understanding through nearness and discourse. And perhaps we may see the highest development of the prophetic consciousness in those prayers and confessions in which Jeremiah[2] is permitted humbly to 'answer back' in the words, 'Ah, Lord God . . .' The prophet is known; and as known, he knows him who is eternally present.

Revelation in the classical sense depends equally on the divine guidance of history and the interpenetration of minds, temporal and eternal. As such its *locus* is the Hebrew nation; for this is the earliest manifestation of the divinely-constituted community in which the conditions are fulfilled. And since we must regard the divine guidance of events as universal, it follows that the interpenetration of minds is the characteristic

[1] R. G. Swinburne, *C.Q.R.* CLXVI, 333 f. (1965).
[2] J. Skinner, *Prophecy and Religion*, 201–230.

of Hebrew prophecy which made it unique as an organ of divine revelation. However, the very necessity for inter-penetration of divine and human minds places an unavoidable limitation upon revelation in the classical sense, precisely because of the limited capacity of the human mind to transcend its temporal conditions. In attempting to apprehend, to think, and to know, after the eternal mode, the temporally conditioned mind is at its fullest stretch, on the fringe of the just possible. Hence of course arise the occasional misapprehensions of Hebrew insight as judged by later and Christian standards, and the progressive nature of the whole process of revelation. The close of the Old Testament period marks a quite definite logical limit.

Thus it is that the fulness of divine revelation in history necessitates a new mode and a new initiative from the side of the eternal, in order to make possible a further response from man. Christianity claims in effect that the Eternal has been manifested under conditions of temporality. 'The Word was made flesh.' The Incarnation is the divine act of condescension, necessary for revelation as for redemption. Redemption lies outside our present discussion. What is vitally important from the point of view of revelation, however, is the bridging of the gap between the eternal and the temporal by the entering into history of One who, while being fully human, comes to the rescue of the limited human capacity for transcending tem-porality. In the New Testament the interpenetration of minds, human and divine, is able to take place at the temporal level. The Teacher-disciple relationship becomes a fuller possibility, a richer encounter, and a deeper understanding. But this is to anticipate.

XIII

TIME AND THE ETERNAL WORD

THE programme which we set ourselves at the end of Chapter IX is nearing completion. Creation, freedom, history, and revelation have occupied our attention already. We come, therefore, to what is the crucial test of any formulation of the relationship between eternity and time: the doctrine of the Incarnation. Granted that the central mystery of the faith is beyond human understanding, we must still make the attempt to relate the earthly life of Jesus of Nazareth to the life of the Eternal God, consistently with the facts of the New Testament and in the light of the position we have now reached.

The classical formulations of orthodoxy, with their reliance on the Greek philosophical tradition as the appropriate vehicle for sustained theological thinking, represent the first maturity of the Christian religion; and this achievement of the patristic age has stood the Church in good stead down to the present century. If it is in need of reconsideration today, the reason lies in the form rather than the content of Christian affirmation. Biblical theology, repudiating the older philosophical categories, attempts indeed to get behind the patristic period, so as to allow the documents of revelation to speak directly to our own age. But the conviction that modern Christianity has in some sense outgrown the patristic formulations has led to a new devotion to peculiarly scriptural categories of thought. To go back to the beginning is laudable enough; and as a first step it has been amply rewarded with new insights into the meaning of the Bible. However, the work of biblical theology is not an end in itself. If the contrast between the thought-forms of the Fathers and those of the modern world is striking, that between first-century Christianity and the present generation of believers is even more so. We are surely right therefore in seeing biblical theology as an exploration of the ground, prior to a new synthesis in more modern terms. Thus, the naïveté of certain conclusions of biblical theologians, notably on the subject of time and its relation to the eternal, is to be regarded not as a permanent element in a valid presentation of Christian belief, but as a challenge to present-day thought. We must not shirk the next step. Our task is to formulate the central truth of the Christian revelation in terms which are consistent with a modern understanding of temporality and its relation to the eternal world. Of course this is a large undertaking. All I shall attempt here is the tentative examination of particular points; but in doing so I hope to demonstrate the usefulness of the view of eternity explored already.

CHRISTOLOGICAL CONFESSION AND ENQUIRY[1]

The life of Jesus of Nazareth defies every human attempt at classification. He was an enigma to his own generation, and in spite of all the theology that has been written he remains an enigma still. Whether in fact he ever claimed divine status and titles during his lifetime (and this is a question which the present state of biblical criticism must leave to some extent open) he certainly became the object of faith to his followers. Through him men have known a new relationship with God, and a new possibility of triumphant living. The ever-present difficulty of all Christological affirmation is to find adequate means of expressing the experience of divinity, which is ours through the life of Jesus of Nazareth, while holding fast to his undoubted Manhood. Who can he be, if he brings us near to the Eternal God; in such manner that we know both righteousness and sin, judgement and reconciliation, death and newness of life, love and self-giving; all in the richness of a single experience, which seizes and transforms our whole being? The first disciples faced the same experience and the same question. The New Testament authors began to formulate the answer; and in a sense the later ontology is already implicit in their

[1] Emphasizing that the doctrine of Chalcedon is not merely negative, R. V. Sellers insists that 'two principles were present in the Church's thought concerning the Person of her Lord from the outset . . . the principle of Christological confession, and . . . the principle of Christological enquiry'. (*The Council of Chalcedon*, xiii). We may see here not only a suitable sub-title but a useful guide to procedure.

writings. When he says that '*God* was *in Christ* reconciling the world unto himself', St Paul is asserting that the Eternal is uniquely present in a particular human life, active for our salvation. And the fourth evangelist goes further still when he employs the *Logos* concept to assert Christ's pre-existence as God, and his entry into a fully human state. It remained only for the Chalcedonian Fathers to exclude all possible heretical understatements, and in their own idiom to safeguard the truth as they saw it: the fulness of the Godhead and the fulness of the Manhood united in the One Person of Christ.

Even though our faith is secure and our orthodoxy unimpeachable, it is well to examine the logical steps on which it is based. We begin by recognizing a clear distinction between activity and ontology. Putting on one side the problems of historicity (which are no part of our present concern) and allowing the New Testament to speak to us in its own manner, we must say that our knowledge is of the activity of Jesus, while our faith is expressed in the ontology of his Person. In other words, the *data* of the Christological problem are the record of what Jesus did, including the attitude which he elicited in his followers; together with our own personal experience of what he still does, again including the attitude which he calls forth in ourselves. Literally that is what is *given*. But while the simple believer need go little further, the enquiring mind of the theologian must attempt to integrate these *data* into a coherent doctrine of Christ's Person. *We* ask who he is, what is his status, how is his being to be characterized. It is only when we ask ontological questions that we arrive at ontological answers. Revelation is not given in propositional form. The Chalcedonian formula as such is not revealed. Revelation is given through historical occurrence, and supremely through the historical activity of a particular Person. If, as Hodgson[1] asserts, the Nicene Fathers 'substituted the statement of a timeless truth for the recitation of an impossible bit of history', what is proclaimed is still the core of an historical revelation, indeed the key to all history. The *revelatum* is the Person of Jesus Christ: not in the sense that valid ontological knowledge of that Person is mysteriously imparted to men, but in the sense that here is the *locus* of the activity which is revelational and redemptive.

[1] L. Hodgson, *The Doctrine of the Trinity*, 67.

Starting from these *data*, given to our apprehension in history and continuing personal experience, we proceed to ask the ontological questions; and the statements of Christological doctrine (whether classical or modern, adequate or inadequate) are the answers humanly given to problems humanly raised.

It is all too easy to dismiss the traditional formulation of the doctrine of the Incarnation as God masquerading as man;[1] but to do so shows little appreciation of the subtlety of the theological problem, nor yet of the distinction (already noted) between ontology and activity. The terms of the problem can be stated simply enough, even if its solution proves ultimately to be beyond our capacity. The word 'divinity' insists on finding its way into anything we say about Jesus. *In Jesus divinity is revealed in a human life.* Yet such a statement of our Christian experience, suitable though it may be as popular exposition, is too loose, to naïve, to rank as a formulation of the truth which theology must safeguard. The quality of 'divinity' cannot be postulated directly of an individual human life, which comes into existence (as ours does) only at a particular moment of history. Theology has to find some way of holding together the divinity and the humanity, the two poles of what is given to Christian experience, without simply identifying a finite human life with the being of God. That is the problem.

(1) The early Fathers tackled the problem, as they were almost bound to do, in terms of universals. Herein lies the strength of their position; but also a certain failure in communication between their age and ours, which has been fruitful of considerable misunderstanding. As conceived in patristic theology, the two natures of Christ, human and divine, are abstractions not directly available to experience. The word 'nature' in this connection denotes that which is common to a class of existents, considered in isolation from the particularity of individuals and the richness of the experience in which individuals are known. 'Human nature' is that which all men share by virtue of being human. It can be defined in terms of finitude, creatureliness, bodily existence, limited freedom, and such like qualities. It is a kind of pigeon-hole into which all men can be fitted; different from the pigeon-holes into which other classes of existents must be fitted, such as things, plants, animals, or angels. Human

[1] J. A. T. Robinson, *Honest to God*, 66.

nature exists, or is held to exist, as a universal: exemplified in particular human beings. The 'divine nature', similarly conceived, is a unit class; characterized by a number of 'attributes' (such as omnipotence, omniscience, and others of an essentially negative form) which are intended to mark a contrast with 'human nature'. The 'divine nature' is that by virtue of which God is God; the 'attributes' those by which deity is deity. And of course it represents an abstraction from the richness of the experience in which deity is known.

The doctrine of the Incarnation in its classical form, so far from being a solution of the Christological problem, merely safeguards the opposite poles of the truth as revealed. Neither the Godhead nor the Manhood of Jesus Christ are to be denied: both natures are affirmed in their fulness, and are declared to be united hypostatically in his Person. As such the doctrine is an affirmation of the ontological implications of what is given to our human experience by the Incarnate Life in its totality. Eminently cautious as a result of examining and refuting opposing heresies, deliberately avoiding the temptation to explain the ultimate mystery in terms which might well have denied some aspect of the complex truth, the Chalcedonian definition has seemed to modern Churchmen to say too little. Recent attempts to improve on the patristic achievement, or at least to enlarge its scope, have frequently misunderstood the concept of 'nature', human or divine, as a universal; just as they have misunderstood 'Person' as an ontological term referring to a discrete centre of being. Modern thought has been characterized very often by the dual attempt to impart greater richness into the word 'nature', and psychological content into the concept of 'Person'. Thus it is that the classical definition, for all its reticence, has been felt to be inadequate as an expression of the truth as it is revealed in Christ Jesus. The study of gospel evidence, by putting renewed emphasis on his humanity, has led to new difficulties in giving adequate expression to his divinity.

The movement which demands a fuller 'explanation' goes back at least to Gore's Bampton Lectures of 1891. It has seemed that the fulness of Christ's humanity, or the reality of his human experience and consciousness, necessitates the suppression of some at least of the divine attributes at the historical moment in which the Incarnation took place. Modern kenotic theories, which fastened onto the well-known text in St Paul (Phil. ii. 7), have attempted to carry the doctrine past the stage of mere affirmation in the hope of reaching some deeper understanding. The self-emptying, or *kenosis*, came to be regarded as a laying aside of the active attributes of Godhead, viz. omnipotence, omniscience, and omnipresence; and thus kenotic Christology implies 'some real modification of the divine attributes as a necessary condition of the true and personal entrance of the Son of God into human history and human experience'.[1] But as A. M. Ramsey[2] has reminded us, the kenotic view rests to some extent on a misunderstanding of the Pauline text, where 'the verb "he emptied himself" has no second object, as if to define that of which He emptied Himself'. The Apostle is dealing, not with ontological questions, but with the humility exemplified by God the Son who 'poured himself out' in becoming Man. Nevertheless, this text continues to provide the biblical starting point for those modern speculations which see some retraction of divinity within the restraint of human nature as we know it; and not a few writers have wrestled with the problem of the conditions to which the Eternal Son was subject when he stooped to unite our human nature to himself for the world's ransoming.

Still speaking within the horizons of classical theology we ask, Can deity be separated from any of its attributes and remain deity? One may answer with Forsyth[3] that in the Incarnate Life omnipotence and omniscience work through the limitations of love; that the only limitation is self-limitation. Indeed it is; but is anything gained by speaking of limitations accepted instead of conditions necessitated? Since nobody supposes that conditions were imposed by any other power than God himself, the difference is merely verbal. A better answer is that of Barth[4]: 'God is always God even in his humiliation . . . . He humbled himself, but he did not do it by ceasing to be who he is.'—i.e. the Incarnation is *sui generis*: it reveals God

---

[1] E. R. Fairweather, in F. W. Beare, *A Commentary on the Epistle to the Philippians*, 160.
[2] A. M. Ramsey, *From Gore to Temple*, 30 f.
[3] P. T. Forsyth, *The Person and Place of Jesus Christ*, 311, 315.
[4] K. Barth, *Church Dogmatics*, IV/1, 179f.

O

as he eternally is, self-giving love. As Ramsey[1] puts it, the attributes 'are not renounced, but rather manifested, in the life and Passion of Christ, in a "new man".'

Temple[2] sought to avoid the difficulties of the kenotic view by suggesting that 'God the Son did indeed most truly live the life recorded in the Gospel, but *added this* to the other work of God'. Realizing this solution to be vulnerable in that 'it appears to make the Incarnation a mere episode in the Life of the Eternal Son', he insisted that it is not 'a *mere* episode', but 'a *revealing* episode'. This suggestion in its turn has been criticized by Quick,[3] Ramsey,[4] and others; both on the ground that it virtually divides the consciousness of the Son, and by the addition of human experiences in effect reimposes limitations. Thus, in spite of somewhat exhaustive exploration, kenotic theories even in a modified form are notoriously difficult to sustain. The difficulties, inherent no doubt in any attempt to go beyond the classical affirmations or to express their content in modern terms, seem to be exaggerated however by the fact that the distinction between time and eternity has been either glossed over or insufficiently allowed for. This aspect of the matter must now be examined.

(2) In stating the elements of the Christological problem, I drew attention to the impropriety of identifying a human life, which comes into existence only at a particular moment of history, with the being of God. Why? Because, however we may use the terms, humanity is temporal while divinity is eternal. The disparity is there whether or not we choose to give to eternity its full philosophical sense of timelessness. Even in the biblical usage a stumbling-block lies concealed; and any attempt to do more than hold the two sides of the classical affirmation in tension inevitably trips up on it. All talk about deity, whether in scripture or in the patristic writings, tends to imprecision for this reason.

If with the biblical authors we take existence in time to be the only conceivable mode of being (and this view appears to be implicit in scripture), we still find need of the phrase 'from

[1] A. M. Ramsey, *loc. cit.*, 39.
[2] W. Temple, *Christus Veritas*, 143 f. (my italics).
[3] O. C. Quick, *Doctrines of the Creed*, 138.
[4] A. M. Ramsey, *loc. cit.*, 41 f.

everlasting to everlasting' if we are to characterize the being of God; for it must be impossible to speak of a time when God is not. If on the other hand we follow the general philosophical tradition and conceive eternity as wholly other than time, we may characterize the being of God as belonging to this timeless order; and then, whether the time-series is finite or infinite, it is again impossible to point to a time at which God is not. Logically these are the only alternatives. Either God is in time, and precedes all other existences in time by his own infinity. Or he is timeless being, and the question of temporal precedence does not arise.

Precisely these same logical alternatives confront us when we ascribe divinity to our Lord Jesus Christ; but the problem is further complicated by the fact that the human life of Jesus belongs certainly to the temporal order. We have to find a way of saying that there is no conceivable time at which he does not exist as God; for otherwise our attempt to speak of his divinity leads straight into either the adoptionist or the Arian heresy (rightly rejected as denials of the truth of Christian experience). If we are working within a world-view which thinks exclusively or implicitly in terms of time, we must conceive the being of the Son also as 'from everlasting to everlasting'. This requirement leads immediately to a doctrine of pre-existence, indeed pre-existence from the beginning of all things. This is the logic of St John's formulation, 'In the beginning was the Word'. Biblical thought was temporally conditioned. Whether the same is true of patristic thought in its entirety is not certain; though there is singularly little evidence to suggest that in their Christological discussion the early Fathers drew upon those elements of the Greek philosophical tradition which were capable of distinguishing the truly eternal (i.e. timeless) from the merely temporal mode of existence. Almost alone in the earlier centuries, St Augustine[1] seems to have appreciated the force of the second alternative: that God the Son does not by time precede time. Even the theology of Chalcedon must apparently be read against a background which knows only a temporal mode of being. Thus, not only is hypostatic union affirmed between disparate 'natures', divine and human, infinite and finite; but union between Being which already has

[1] Augustine, *Confessions*, Bk. XI, 13.

an infinitely extended 'history' in time and being which came into existence at a particular moment of time. This, I believe, is a valid observation whether we think of the 'human nature' as that of the new creation born in Bethlehem, or as the universal which may be said to ante-date human history.

If any progress is to be made, the being of God must be conceived as truly eternal—unchanging, and unconditioned in any temporal sense. How far the Godhead can be adequately characterized in his eternal being by a list of attributes, designed to mark a contrast with temporal man, is beside the point, until he is fully revealed under such circumstances as he chooses in his sovereign freedom. Then, but only then, the divine attributes may legitimately be read back into his eternal being, in accordance with the principle that the revelation is necessarily true to that which is revealed. We can start only from the Christological *data* of experience. And primarily this is the basis of faith: that in Christ we have knowledge of Deity in and through a human life. Having created human life, and willing to draw humanity to himself, God reveals himself in humanity. Yet 'God in Christ' must remain logically distinct from 'God in his eternal being'.

We secure the reality of the Incarnation in accordance with scripture by use of the Pauline phrase, *God was in Christ*. The operative word, that carries all the weight of interpretation, is 'in'. We mean much more than an 'indwelling', even if we add 'in a unique manner'; for 'indwelling' is used of the Spirit in relation to man as redeemed. The words, 'unite', 'reside', 'possess', all suggest themselves for the resolution of our verbal difficulty; and not one of them is entirely adequate, though the classical 'unite' undoubtedly comes nearest. St Paul's phrase, taken out of context though it is, must be allowed to tell its own story; and the *in* must carry the weight of meaning, if we are to remain true to the scriptural position, refusing to prejudge the questions of ontology by the choice of any other word. Nevertheless, this somewhat general statement, *God was in Christ*, itself implies an ontology of Christ's Person: one which requires formulation in terms not of abstract natures but of the distinction between the temporal and the eternal modes of being.

Human life is 'from a beginning' and 'towards an end'. Divine life is eternal, timeless, without beginning and without

end. If then Deity is *in* a particular human life, it means that
from the moment of conception that human life perfectly
expresses God himself (not some, or even all, of his attributes)
in the circumstances of temporal existence. We recall that the
Logos Christology of the fourth gospel is supplemented by the
corresponding passage in the first epistle of St John: 'The life
was manifested . . . the eternal life, which was with the Father'
(1 John i. 2); reading ζωὴν τὴν αἰώνιον as 'timeless life',
because only the full sense of eternal is adequate to the
understanding of the revelation of God in Christ. The
Incarnation is the showing forth of Life—albeit life of an
eternal quality, yet manifested in temporality. The eternal
'shone through' the temporal, so to speak. But to say this is not
to fall back on Robinson's[1] analogy of a window. A window is a
static, passive, thing. Its only relevant property is its transparency. While transparency may take us part of the way, it
is a wholly inadequate concept. 'He that hath seen me hath
seen the Father'. You don't see a window: you see through it.
But to see Christ is to 'see' the Father; because 'I am *in* the
Father, and the Father *in* me'. (John xiv. 9, 10) The Eternal is
disclosed in his mysterious activity through (i.e. by being
embodied *in*) the temporal. Timeless life is revealed in time.
The same life which knows neither beginning nor ending was
manifested *in* a human life which moved purposively from a
beginning in time to an end in time.[2]

So far, however, from the Incarnate life being an 'episode'
in the life of the Godhead, it is not even possible to assert that
from the point of view of Deity there was any lapse of time
between the historical moments of the Conception and the
Ascension. In accordance with our general thesis, we must
regard these two moments as simultaneous from the stand-
point of eternity: *strictly* simultaneous, not merely relatively
near together by contrast with an everlasting span of time. And
here the concept of the Creative Word again comes to our aid.
Just as the Creative Word, in the eternal 'now', issues in the

---

[1] J. A. T. Robinson, *Honest to God*, 71.

[2] To put the matter in this way is not intended to deny the continuation of the
Incarnate life (under a different mode) 'after' the 'event' which we call the
'Ascension'. Nor in treating the temporal span of the Incarnation as from Conception to Ascension is it intended to deny the sense in which the Church and
sacraments are its continuation.

whole drama of created history, 'spreading out' into temporal activity (Cf. Figure 5); so the Logos himself, willing to reveal the life of God fully (so far as human existence permits) issues in the Incarnate life 'spread out' in time from Conception to Ascension. The thirty years of the Incarnate life must not be thought of as an interval from the stand-point of eternity.

The being of the Eternal Son is Love—filial love which perfectly mirrors and responds to the love of the Father. Within the temporal span of the Incarnate life that same love is active historically: perfectly towards the Father as filial, perfectly towards mankind as redemptive: one with the love of God in his eternal life. If, in the light of the Incarnation, we speak of divine omnipotence, it is of the omnipotence of love. Divine omniscience is to be seen primarily as that inside knowledge of all men through the eyes of love which we find in Jesus. If in the eternal mode of being omniscience must still be taken to mean the totality of all possible knowledge, clearly its adjustment to a temporal mode implies the acceptance of a human perspective rather than a limitation so-called. What we have to assert before all else is that the Incarnate life reveals the life of God so perfectly that we can *know* the Godhead *only as self-revealed*. It is pointless to specify a number of attributes *a priori*, and then to enquire how far these can or cannot be revealed under the conditions of a temporal existence.

Have we then arrived at an ontology of the Incarnate life, which is in any sense adequate as a solution of the Christological problem? Perhaps not. But in emphasizing the contrast between the temporal and the eternal, we have surely moved in the right direction. The most we can say at present is that the temporal existence of the Christ, extending from Conception to Ascension, while remaining a truly human existence, is so permeated by divinity that it reveals the eternal life of God the Son in relation to the Father and to the human race; and by the omnipotence of divine love active on the temporal plane the redemptive sacrifice is completed, which was willed eternally by the Word.

THE ETERNAL CHRIST

In Christ, God and Man are One. This is the truth which the

Chalcedonian formula safeguards. It is the condition under which revelation, defined previously in terms of the inter-penetration of minds as between Master and disciple, can occur in all fulness: it is the prerequisite of effectual redemption. Revelation and redemption belong to the temporal phase of the Incarnation; but Christian faith has always held that God the Son, having taken human nature upon himself, remains Man. This item of faith too requires further elucidation in terms of the relation between time and eternity.

There is no doubt that the doctrines of the heavenly inter-cession and the continuing priesthood of Christ were formulated in the first instance against a background of everlasting time, rather than in terms of a true eternity. (Heb. vii. 24, 25) The point made both by scripture and doctrine may be put in this way: When Christ's visible presence was withdrawn from this earthly sphere, the ontological fact of the Incarnation continues in the heavenly 'places'. In his continuing life with the Father, he remains both God and Man. In his continuing Manhood he is both Intercessor and High Priest. And in the inadequate language of temporality this second phase of the Incarnate life is thought of as 'beginning' at the Ascension.

Now clearly this last phrase must be taken as relating the truth of the Ascended life of Christ to our human time-scale. From that moment onwards in our temporal experience Christ is both God and Man in the heavenlies, and continues so until the end of our time. Even though the same time-scale was assumed uncritically to be applicable to the being of God Incarnate, we are under no obligation to think in this way. Indeed, recognizing the simultaneity of the eternal mode of being, we must say rather that as a result of the Incarnation Christ is eternally God and Man. Nevertheless, a temporal element still lurks even in this statement, which may become the cause of real misapprehension. For implicitly we make a distinction between the being of God the Son before and after the moment of Incarnation, suggesting that a real change took place. This moment, however, is relative to our time-scale. What significance has it from the stand-point of eternity? We want to say that before the moment of Incarnation, as referred to our time-scale, God the Son was God but not Man; whereas after the moment of Incarnation, as referred to our time-scale, God the Son is both God and Man. This is a meaningful statement in terms of time, but still meaningless in terms of eternity. If we speak of 'pre-existence', we are improperly combining a temporal 'pre-' with an eternal 'existence'. It seems that human language fails at this point. Or rather, that human logic is incapable of penetrating the mystery of Incarnation from the point of view of eternity.

Some progress is possible perhaps if we look at the matter psychologically—though this may appear a poor substitute for a consistent ontology. We may say that from the stand-point of God the Incarnation meant a sharing at first hand in the experience of temporal existence, an effectual participation in history. Then part of the truth of the Ascension is that God the Son retains the memory and the marks of that experience. This appears to be implied by Hebrews ii. 18: 'For in that he himself hath suffered being tempted, he is able to succour them that are tempted'; and by Hebrews iv. 15: 'For we have not a high priest that cannot be touched with the feeling of our infirmities; but one that hath been in all points tempted like as we are, yet without sin.' Clearly these texts refer to the Ascended Christ, not to Christ during his earthly life; and they imply at least a memory of direct human experience. He knows what it is to be a man, because he has lived an earthly life in time. He can care, because he knows our human condition from actual experience. He can succour us, because he died and rose again for our salvation.

But does what we have called 'memory' imply any sort of continuing temporality in the being of him who has experienced temporality? Memory is the faculty of recalling the past into the present. Apart from the past-present distinction 'memory' is devoid of significance. We ascribe to the Ascended Christ the ability still to share in the experience of temporality which is inherent in memory. But this is not all. If memory is the recalling of the past into the present, what is remembered must in some sense be imprinted on personality by experience. Should we not take seriously then the humanity which Christ shared with us, and in full reverence attempt to draw out its eternal implications? Through earthly experience any other man builds up a personality which is potentially eternal; incorporating every element of that experience into his being, which consequently is chronologically structured. This is the basis of continuing identity, both here and hereafter. If we would do full justice to Christ's humanity, we shall not shrink from suggesting that he too developed as Man in precisely this sense. And the New Testament leaves us not without clear hints that this was so. Not only is it said that 'Jesus advanced in wisdom and stature' (Lk. ii. 52), but that, 'though he was a Son, yet (he) learned obedience by the things which he suffered', being 'made perfect' (Heb. v. 8 f). Somewhat as the ordinary man builds up a personality which is potentially eternal, so with all reverence and very tentatively we are suggesting that God the Son integrated into his already eternal being all those elements of earthly experience which he accepted and transformed; that his being includes chronological structure too. The reality of conscious human existence is thereby secured in our thinking about the Lord's Incarnation.

Thus, we can say that from the standpoint of eternity the Incarnation involves the taking-up of temporality as a mode of experience, and as a continuing content of conscious life, into the Godhead. This undoubtedly helps. But it does not resolve the logical impasse which fogs our essentially temporal manner of thinking. For it is still not possible to point to a *moment* in the *divine* existence at which this new mode of experience *begins*. Since the Incarnation implies full participation of the Eternal in temporal life, and full acceptance of the development of human personality in time which such participation entails, from the point of view of temporal existence we think of something added to divinity. Within the limits of human language and logic we appear to be justified in regarding the Incarnation as the *taking-up of temporality into the Eternal*. But we can preserve the reality of eternal being only by insisting that it was always the divine purpose to do this, and by refusing to make the distinction between divine will and its achievement in the eternal world. If we would think correctly of the Incarnation as an eternal reality, we shall not speak of it as an 'episode' in the life of Deity, nor even as a 'revealing episode'. Instead, the taking-up of temporality into the Eternal must be considered under two aspects:

(1) A particular span of temporality, with its humiliation and attendant Passion, is eternally present to Deity. From the point

of view of time, this span of temporality has a 'before' and an
'after'. Thus, speaking in terms of a time-scale, we say that
before the human conception of Jesus, the Son was fully God
with the Father ('In the beginning was the Word, and the
Word was with God, and the Word was God'); but that the
Son was not yet Man. The 'not yet' betrays our temporal thinking. And, still in terms of time, we say that after the Ascension
the Incarnate Lord, God and Man, presents our perfected
manhood in the heavenlies. The span of temporality, however,
intervening between the earthly events of Conception and
Ascension, is eternally purposed, eternally experienced, even
eternally remembered; because in the 'eternal now' will, and
act, and knowledge belong together. Divine Love bears the
pain and rebellion of the creation in one single self-giving act;
which, temporally-considered, spreads out as successiveness in
the Incarnate life on earth. But since patripassianism has rightly
been declared heretical, we are careful to think of the *Son* as
that Person of the Blessed Trinity to whom the crucial span of
temporal history is eternally present. *He* is Incarnate. *He*
suffered and triumphed in time. *He* holds within himself the
redeeming span of temporality in his eternal being; presenting
it before the Father on our behalf.

(2) The Incarnation, being the incorporation of the temporal
into the Eternal, completes and perfects creation through
redemption. Christ is the New Creation into whom all created
being must be drawn, and in whom man as redeemed receives
his new status of sonship. In saying 'must be drawn' we are
using the language of time: i.e. before the Incarnation took
place in history the new status was not yet given as a fact of
temporal life; whereas after the Incarnation has taken place
it can be received by faith, proleptically in this temporal
existence, and fully in the eternal world which man is destined
to enter. But again in the eternal world the 'result', or ontological outcome, of the Incarnation for created man is always a
completed achievement in the timeless 'now'. Creation,
redemption, new creation in Christ, adoption to sonship, are
strictly simultaneous in that eternal reality which, though it
knows time directly through the Incarnate experience of the
Son, is essentially timeless.

Thus, not only is eternal life a present possession of those who are 'in Christ' here and now by faith (though a possession to be entered upon fully only hereafter), but the salvation which Jesus came to bring is available to all men; irrespective of whether they lived before Christ or after, irrespective of whether they have yet heard the Gospel or not. Where classical theology must say that 'human nature' is united to God in Christ by the fact of the Incarnation (and by speaking in terms of universals may fail in communication with our age), we may say that through faith in Christ and in his sacrifice all men (as individuals), whether they come to belief in this life or hereafter, are taken up in their temporality into union with the Eternal in the Incarnate Son. Salvation is for all men, on the condition of faith in Christ, because all men belong to that temporal history the crucial span of which the Son has taken up into his eternal being. All believers, past, present, and future, are one in him; and in him are presented before the Throne of Grace, where they unite their worship and self-giving with his perfect offering. If in the Incarnation, regarded as an event of time, the Eternal Love spreads out into the crucial span of temporality; by the reverse process salvation draws the whole of temporal history together into its eternal fulfilment in Christ in the timeless 'now' which is the mode of ultimate Reality.

XIV

EPILOGUE: AN END OF TIME

CULLMANN makes much of the central place of the Christ-event in the 'linear time' presupposed by the biblical authors; and if by central he means 'supremely significant' nobody will quarrel with him. History, if not time, is divided by the Christ-event into preparation and fulfilment. But he seems to mean more. Indeed he insists on retaining primitive temporal concepts as integral to Christianity, so giving an extraordinarily literal interpretation to those texts which refer to the *parousia*. Though, as he asserts rightly, the Christian attitude to eschatology renders the date of the *parousia* theologically irrelevant, yet it is of a future event in time and upon earth that he writes.[1] Here if anywhere in the New Testament is the place for radical re-interpretation. It is imperative for twentieth-century faith that the essential truth of Christian expectation should be expressed with a proper regard for the status of time, and in a setting of greater cosmic significance than the three dimensions of our embodied existence on earth.

Of course it goes without saying that the earliest Christians could conceive of Judgement, the final victory of the Kingdom, and the resurrection of the faithful in Christ, in no other terms. We have accustomed ourselves to a larger view of the created universe, in which the anthropocentric outlook on space and time has lost its meaning. What does the 'end of time', or 'the end of the age', mean to us today? Certainly not a kind of final curtain on the entire created order; though the possibility of nuclear destruction may indeed lead us to envisage such a curtain for human history. No; the existence of man, as an individual, is itself 'towards an end', a natural end which demands to be understood. This surely is sufficient basis for a

---

[1] O. Cullmann, *Christ and Time*, 139–43.

Christian eschatology. The end of our earthly life is pregnant
with spiritual significance for each one of us. Can we not relate
this end to the Christian expectation, in such a way as to do full
justice to the essential insights of the New Testament?

What happens to human life at death? Humanly speaking
we can do no more than anticipate the imminent end, not only
of activity but of individual subjective time. The pessimism, as
well as the truth, of modern existentialism is reflected in that
disturbing phrase, 'towards an end'. Christian faith suggests an
answer; which is by no means tied to a false dichotomy of body
and soul. Beyond the moment of death it places Judgement, and
finally Resurrection. But any attentive reading of the New
Testament discloses that both judgement and resurrection span
the dividing line between the 'here' and the 'hereafter'.

In the thought of the fourth evangelist judgement operates
first of all in this life. 'This is the judgement, that the light is
come into the world, and men loved the darkness rather than
the light' (John iii. 19). Each man is judged, here and now, by
his attitude to Christ. Human society as a whole is judged, here
and now, by the eschatological event of the Cross as it is
interpreted by the Spirit. (John xvi. 8–11). The judgement
which man passes on himself, as he journeys through time, must
of necessity harden into a final judgement, which he will reap
at the end. Eternal life, offered to men here and now in the
gospel as a present possession, is essentially a sharing in the
Risen Life of Christ, an anticipation of the general resurrection.
Yet what is experienced proleptically in this life will be known
and possessed in its fullness in the life to come. Thus, judgement
and resurrection are both present and future. Both have their
place here: both have their place hereafter. But to speak of
final judgement and general resurrection as future is not
necessarily to locate them in time. The most we can do is to
locate in future time the moment at which we enter the
hereafter: and this is the moment of death.

We still ask, what happens at death? Or to frame the question
more appropriately in the light of our previous discussions,
How can we usefully think of the state which lies beyond the
end of our subjective time? St Paul, in a passage which is
evocative rather than factually informative, writes: 'If we
believe that Jesus died and rose again, even so them also that

are fallen asleep in Jesus will God bring with him' (1 Thess.
iv. 14). We read in the fourth gospel: 'Our friend Lazarus is
fallen asleep . . . . Now Jesus had spoken of his death' (John
xi. 11, 13). Even if the analogy of sleep is a somewhat obvious
euphemism for death, at least it has strong New Testament
support, and has been good Christian currency ever since. Little
though we can know of the intermediate state, it is sufficient
that we should think of the faithful departed as 'asleep in
Jesus'. The image is a powerful one, when we recall that to
awake out of sleep is the beginning of new life to all intents and
purposes.

The Christian who has fallen asleep in Jesus has passed out
of this temporal existence; though, as we have suggested,
temporality still clings to him. Jesus too passed out of this temporal existence, and (in the language of time) 'returned' to
the eternal world: the temporality of his earthly life is taken up
into his eternal mode of being. These considerations point to
what we can only call the eternal world (in spite of some
persistence of temporality, at least during a 'period' of purification) as the 'place' where the promises will be fulfilled. Christ
is risen and ascended. We share proleptically in his risen life.
The Christian hope is that we shall be drawn more perfectly
into that life beyond the grave. The fulfilment of our expectation
indeed belongs to the future when referred to our present
temporal existence. It can take place, however, only in the
conditions of eternity; for the end of time, subjectively for
every man the moment of death, marks our entry into the
eternal mode. If our sleeping in Jesus can be thought of as a
purification and a healing, we may believe that we shall awake
to his presence in glory in the Kingdom of the Father. Awaking
to the presence of the Eternal Christ, we shall know as we have
been known, in that eternal experience which is truly timeless.

It is in this sense, I believe, that time must pass away. For
each one of us individually the frittering movement and the
purposeful growth, which alike belong to the temporal order,
must come to rest ultimately in an 'eternal now'. And though
for many too active folk such an idea may be disturbing in the
extreme, it is not to be lightly set aside as an expression (albeit
inadequate) of final blessedness. 'Be still then and know that
I am God'—how hard we find it! Yet worship is just that.

True, the activity of worship under conditions of temporality itself partakes of temporality. An act of worship endures through a period of time: it has a temporal structure of words and action: but its heart is pure adoration. In worship, as we know it, the temporal is but the sacramental embodiment of the thing itself in its eternal stillness. Few of us are entirely without the experience that in worship time stands still: its passage registered by the clock but not in consciousness. Need we doubt that this strange but nearly universal experience is a parable pointing the mind towards, and already anticipating, the eternal goal? Other figures too have their place, and the New Testament is rich in suggestions, but this pointer which touches the heart of the matter should be allowed to guide our thinking and to form our conception of the final state. Eternity is the goal: temporality marks the way.

* * *

We must now try to draw together a long and perplexing discussion of the diverse aspects of our experience. Immersed as we are in temporality, we find ultimate meaning in the eternal. Christian theology, based empirically on revelation but drawing too on the insights of scientists and philosophers, is our window on to eternal reality. As Tillich[1] has reminded us, theology moves backwards and forwards between 'the eternal truth of its foundation and the temporal situation in which the eternal truth must be received.' The conceptual framework within which it operates is one in which change and permanence, time and eternity, are contrasting elements. We are inclined to make a sharp distinction between time, as the symbol of the changing, and eternity, as the symbol of the permanent. We should not forget, however, that these abstractions from the richer fulness of what is given are no more than the conceptual tools which we forge for talking about that experience. There is a real danger that discussion and analysis may divide a unity, which is given, into disparate and wholly unconnected spheres. There is only one world: not two. We must discriminate without dividing. If we take seriously the fundamental insight that the temporal and the eternal interpenetrate, we shall avoid that fatal fragmentation of reality to which all conceptual discussion is prone.

[1] P. Tillich, *Systematic Theology*, I, 3.

The ever-changing present of the individual consciousness is the *locus* of the interpenetration of the temporal and the eternal. But the conscious life of the self, though intimately known, is enigmatic to a degree. Who am I? what am I? if the temporal and the eternal impinge upon me in my conscious life; the one conditioning me, the other drawing me out of myself to find my *patria* elsewhere. Divided, torn asunder; seeking, but seldom finding; man is a stranger to himself. There moved once on the plane of history a human Life, the same yet utterly different, in which man can learn to see the Image of what he himself would be. To find the Christ, or rather to be found by him, is the liberating experience which brings meaning and a goal into our fragmented condition. 'The Word was made flesh, and dwelt among us'—so this world has eternal significance. 'God was in Christ reconciling the world unto himself'—so we are sons in a Father's house. The Incarnational participation of God the Son in the sufferings and frustrations of our temporality, which is the supreme expression and revelation of Eternal Love, restores the unity which we seek but constantly destroy. In the Eternal Christ we find the true interpenetration of the temporal and the eternal. True interpenetration, because the Eternal has taken up the temporal into his own being, once for us all.

The coming-down of a richer reality into the life of man transforms the merely temporal, lifting it up into the eternal, recreating or completing the unity we seek. May we not say that the unity of eternity and time is the holding-together in perfect balance in the Life of the Blessed Trinity of two diverse modes of experience? The one is the mode of Reality itself: the other the mode given initially to the created order as the condition of its creatureliness, which it must transcend by grace if the goal is to be attained. All creation flows from the 'Father of lights, with whom is no variableness, neither shadow of turning'. Restored, newly created, through the redemptive out-going of the Son and in Holy Spirit, all must return whence it came. The transient and the unchanging are mysteriously bound together, though often we fail to see it so. The temporality of the created order, man's life with its strivings and failures, sufferings and frustrations, is wrapped round and enclosed in the eternity of Creative Love. For each created consciousness, as it finds its true home in eternity, time is at an end. What was distantly perceived becomes present reality. What has been painfully built remains whole for ever. What has been nurtured and transformed bows down in worship. 'Unto the King eternal, immortal, invisible, the only wise God, be honour and glory for ever and ever.'

INDEX OF PROPER NAMES

Alexander, P., 183 n.
Alexander, S., 72 n.
Aristotle, 16 f., 46 f., 55
Aquinas, Thomas, 74 n., 159
Augustine, St., 17, 25 n., 74, 98,
  145, 196, 211
Ayer, A. J., 58

Barr, J., 28 f., 31, 35–9
Barth, K., 209
Beethoven, L. van, 80
Bergson, H., 84, 114, 122
Berlin, I., 190 f.
Boethius, 149 n.
Bohr, N., 182
Boltzmann, L., 62
Boman, T., 77 n.
Brabant, F. H., 31, 147, 149 n.,
  151, 159 n.
Bridgman, P. W., 64 n., 125 n.,
  173 n.
Broad, C. D., 143
Buchan, J., 192, 194
Butterfield, H., 195

Churchill, W. S., 192
Clark, W. E. LeGros, 113 n.
Clausius, R., 59
Crombie, I. M., 103
Cullmann, O., 28, 33–6, 39 f.,
  145, 220

Darwin, C., 76, 106, 114, 116
De Beauregard, O. C., 63 f.,
  137, 156 n.
De Chardin, T., 121
Doppler, C. J., 93
Dunne, J. W., 150 n.

Eddington, A. S., 57, 73
Einstein, A., 49, 123–36, 154
Epstein, I., 195

Fairweather, E. R., 209 n.
Farrer, A., 181
Fizeau, H., 127
Flew, A., 103
Forrest, W. W., 70 n.
Forsyth, P. T., 209

Galileo, 47
Gillispie, C. C., 59 n.
Gore, C., 208

Haldane, J. B. S., 116 n.
Hamner, K. C., 43 n.
Hare, R. M., 105
Heidegger, M., 18 f., 54, 159,
  167
Heim, K., 169 n.
Hodgson, L., 140 n., 206
Hoyle, F., 94
Hubble, E. P., 93, 96 f.
Huxley, J., 114 n.
Huxley, T. H., 106

Isaiah, 80

Jacob, 80
Jeremiah, 202

Kant, E., 17, 143
Kepler, J., 49
Kirk, K. E., 155 n.

Lack, D., 116 n.
Laplace, P. S., 169, 176

P*

Laslett, P., 58, 177 n.
Lazarus, 163, 222
Lemaitre, G., 94
Locke, J., 136
Lovell, A. C. B., 94
Lyttleton, R. A., 109 n.

Mackenzie, J. S., 19
MacLeod, R. B., 42
Marsh, J., 28–31, 39, 145
Mascall, E. L., 74 n., 82, 171 n.
McCrea, W. H., 93 n., 100 n.
McVittie, G. C., 91 n., 93 n.
Medawar, P. B., 121 n.
Michelson, A., 128
Milne, E. A., 74
Minkowski, H., 134–7
Moses, 80

Newton, I., 17, 49, 123, 136

Oparin, A. I., 112 n.
Otto, R., 80

Paley, W., 85
Plato, 16, 145
Polanyi, M., 45 n.
Prigogine, I., 69

Quick, O. C., 84 ff., 210

Ramsey, A. M., 209 f.
Ramsey, I. T., 25 f., 87, 146
Raven, C. E., 114, 116 n.
Richardson, A., 192, 196 n.
Robinson, J. A. T., 148 n.,
   207 n., 213
Rutten, M. G., 111 n., 112 n.
Ryle, G., 176 f.

Sayers, D., 163
Sellers, R. V., 205 n.
Shepherd, A. P., 20, 150 n., 165
Skinner, J., 202 n.
Stoward, P. J., 70 n.
Swinburne, R. G., 149 n., 202

Temple, W., 83, 147 n., 177 n.,
   210
Thornton, L. S., 177 n.
Tillich, P., 223
Toynbee, A., 193

Wallace, A. R., 112
Weyl, H., 136 n.
Whitrow, G. J., 43 n., 59, 72 n.,
   74, 130 n., 136 n.
Wilberforce, S., 106

INDEX OF SUBJECTS

Activity, and ontology, 206 f.
Adaptation, 114, 118
aion, 28, 33–6
Analysis, linguistic, 81, 103 f.
Analogy,
  artist, 84–8, 161, 198 f.
  blind man, 92
  craftsman, 85
  dramatist, 97, 102, 122, 153, 161 ff.
Animism, 172, 183
Atmosphere, 111 f.
Attributes, divine, 208–14
Ascension,
  of Christ, 213 f.
  meaning of, 215–18
Autonomy, 183 f.

Beauty, 21
Being, necessary and contingent, 82 f., 85, 87
Birds, navigation of, 43
blik, 105
Body-mind distinction, 177

Cambrian, 110, 113
Casual, in history, 191–4
Causality, 56 f., 63 ff., 81 f., 168–75
  efficient, 81
  in nervous system, 180–4
  phenomenal, 172 f.
  principle imposed on environment, 178
  validity of concept, 174, 182 f.
Cause,
  First, 82
  classical distinctions, 171

Cause:—*continued*.
  personal category, 170 f., 182 f.
Cell, biological, 43
Change,
  biological, 46 f., 54 f., 69
  genetic, 106, 114 f., 118
  and identity, 151
Changelessness, of God, safeguarded, 150 f.
Choice, 169, 183 ff.
Christ, development as man, 217
Christology, 205–19
  empirical data, 206, 212
  problem stated, 207
Chromosome, 114
chronos, 28–31
Cinematograph, 150, 185
Clock,
  biological, 44–7, 68–71
  paradox, 131
  quartz, 52 f.
  water, 48
Colour,
  change, 43
  distinction of, 45
Complementarity, 182
Conception, of Chirst, 213 f., 218
Consciousness, and environment, 176 ff.
Consistency, in time-keeping, 49–54
Continuity, personal, 150
Cosmology, 90–5
  and creation, 95–102

Creation,
 continuous, 94–7
 doctrine of, 76–89, 147, 151 f.
  157–67
 ex nihilo, 74, 76, 80, 87, 98
 goodness of, 78
 man, 101
 narrative, 77–81
 new, 121, 212, 218
 planetary systems, 99–101
 scientific term, 96 f.
 vindicated, 104 f.
Cross, key to history, 196
Culture, relevance of, 187 f.,
  199
Cybernetics, 64
Cycle, thermodynamic, 60 f.

Dating, geological, 110
Death, 58, 75 n., 221 f.
Deification, 167
Destruction, nuclear, 220
Determinism, 168 f., 175, 183
 historical, 188 ff.
deus ex machina, 169
Dichotomy, body and soul, 220
Dilatation, of time, 130 f.
Dimension, fourth, 133–8
Discipleship, 200 f.
Distance, astronomical, 92
Divine image, 155 f., 164, 200
Divinity, of Christ, 205, 211
Drama, temporal structure, 86 f.
Duration, 15, 145

Earth,
 age of, 72, 95, 110
 interior of, 109
 origin of, 95, 100, 109
Electroencephalogram, 42
Embodiment, of eternal in temporal, 212 f.
Energy, degradation, 61 f., 65–8,
  158, 162

Entropy,
 definition, 60
 law of, 57–75, 158 f., 166
 negative, 63 f.
 and time, 66–71
 and universe, 94
Epiphenomenalism, 45, 164, 181
Episode, revealing, 210, 213, 217
Eschatology, 75 n., 220 f.
Etching, 162 f.
Eternity,
 biblical conception, 33, 38
 philosophical conception,
  19–23
Everlasting, 23–6, 141–5
 contrasted with eternal, 23,
  145, 152
 to everlasting, 141 f., 211
Environment, effect of, 106,
  114, 118
Evil, 162 f.
Evolution,
 biological, 106–22
 cosmic, 94
 creative, 84, 122
 fact and theory, 112, 116
 meaning of word, 107
Existentialism, not teleological,
  159
Experiment, possibility of, 91,
  108

Fall, The, 101
Falsification, 91
'Finger of God', 192
Forces, historical, 189 f.
Fore-calculation, 169
Fore-knowledge, 168 ff., 176,
  184 ff., 198
Fossils, 110, 112
Frame, inertial, 132, 136, 153
Free-will, 176, 179–86
 dramatic, 87, 153
Fundamentalist, 106

Galaxies, recession of, 93 f.
Gaps, God of the, 116
Gardener, invisible, 103
Genesis i, 77–81, 87, 118, 121
Geology, evidence of, 108 ff.
Geometry, Euclidean, 125, 127, 136
'Ghost in machine', 176, 177 n., 181
Gnosticism, 172
God,
    as known, 80
    unchanging, 141 f., 145–8
Goodness, 21
Guidance, divine, of evolution, 115 f., 119

'Hand of God', 190, 195
Heredity, 106, 113
History,
    divine control of, 30–4, 39, 141, 188–98
    of Incarnate Life, 218 f.
    Lord of, 77, 89
    nature of, 187
Honey bee, 43
Hope, Christian, 165 ff.
Horology, 41
Humanity, of Christ, 208

Ideas, Platonic, 16, 145, 147
Identity, personal, 150 f.
I-knowledge, 182
Impropriety, logical, 26, 80, 87, 186
Incarnation, doctrine of, 147, 151 f., 205–19
    in other worlds, 101
Indwelling, 212
Information, theory of, 57 ff., 63 ff.
Insight, Christian, 105
Intercession, heavenly, 215

Interpenetration,
    of minds, 200–3, 215
    temporal and eternal, 224
Interpretation, contrasted with explanation, 100 f., 119 f., 164 n.
Interpretation, prophetic, 194
Interpretation, theological, principle, 88 f.
    of cosmology, 97 ff., 102
    of evolution, 115–22
    of history, 191–6
It-knowledge, 179, 182 f.

Judgement,
    divine, 194, 197
    historical, 191, 194 ff.
    present and future, 221

kairos, 28–36
Kenoticism, 209 f.
Knowledge,
    eternal mode, 148–51, 156 f., 175, 185 f., 198
    modifies knower, 151
    personal, 45, 47, 50, 55

Language,
    confusion of, 180
    parallel, 181 ff.
    religious, 23–6, 146, 186
Laser, 53
Laws of nature, status of, 99, 117 ff.
Levels of being, 177
Libertarianism, 168 f., 175, 183
Life,
    eternal, 23 f., 166, 213, 218, 221
    origin of, 107 f., 111, 119
Light-signalling, 124–30
Light,
    velocity of, 53 f., 91 f., 94, 124, 154
    constancy, 127 f., 130
    determination of, 127

Logos-concept, 206, 213
Love, 163 f., 214, 218, 224

Man, origin of, 113, 119 f., 164
Mating, 114
Meaning, discernment of, 199 f.
Mechanist, 106
Memory, 58, 150
 of Christ, 216
Meson, 131 n.
Metaphysics, traditional, 81 ff.,
 87
Mind,
 conscious, 58
 primacy of, 55 n.
Mind-brain relationship, 58 f.,
 169, 180 ff.
Model, linguistic, 25 f., 87, 146
Motion,
 in sense of change, 16 f.
 perpetual, 60, 68
Motivation,
 historical, 188 f.
 personal, 183
Motor action, 180
Music, temporal structure, 86
Mutation, 111, 113 f., 118
 successive, 116
Myth, Babylonian, 78

Natures, human and divine,
 207 f., 211
Neuro-physiology, 58 f., 170,
 180–3
Neutrality, 196
Novelty, 84, 98 f., 102, 106 f.,
 117, 119 f., 122
Numinous, 80

Objective, distinguished from
 subjective, 44 f.
Observation,
 astronomical, 91 f., 123–6
 procedures of, 123 f., 137

Observers, equivalence of, 93
Omnipotence, 197, 208 f., 214
Omnipresence, 147, 209
Omniscience, 168, 175 f., 183 ff.,
 197 f., 208 f., 214
Ontology, classical, 206 ff.
Order-disorder, 62, 158, 162 f.
Organization, biological, 70
Origin of Species, 106
Orthodoxy,
 biological, 114 f., 119
 Chalcedonian, 206 ff.
'Other human races', 101 f.

Pantheon, 192, 194
parousia, 35, 220
Particularity, 188
Patripassianism, 218
Pattern, of world-lines, 161 ff.
Perception, sense, 180
Personality, outstanding, 189,
 191, 193
Perspective,
 temporal, 131
 contrasted with eternal, 174 f.,
 184 f.
 transcended, 201 ff.
Photo-periodism, 43
Photo-synthesis, 111, 115
Point-event, 133
Positivism, 102–5
Potentiality, of eternal, 165 ff.
Pre-existence, 206, 211, 216
Presuppositions, of history, 193,
 196
Priesthood, of Christ, 215 f., 218
Principle,
 cosmological, 93 f.
 perfect, 94, 96
Process,
 creative, 107 f., 115, 119 f.
 irreversible, 61, 63, 69
 random, 89, 99 f., 102, 104,
 114 f.

Process—*continued*
 reversible, 61
Proto-life, 111 f.
Psychology, child, 45
Psycho-somatic unity, 55 n.
Pulse, 47
Purification, progressive, 166 f., 222
Purpose, divine, 85, 98 f., 102, 117–20, 147, 152, 161 ff., 175, 194, 197, 217

Qualifier, linguistic, 25 f., 87. 146
Quasi-stellar object, 95
Quicunque vult, 101

Radio-activity, 109 f.
Radio-astronomy, 95
Randomness, not irrational, 117 f.
Redemption, 147, 151, 218 f.
Red-shift, 92
Regress, infinite, 92
Relativity, theory of, 49, 53, 63 n., 123–38, 153–7
Representation, non-temporal, 156 f., 160
Responsibility, human, 169, 179, 184, 198
Resurrection,
 of the body, 166 f.
 of Christ, 196
 of the faithful, 221
Revelation, 147 f., 151 f., 187 f., 199–203
 through events, 187, 206
 progressive, 141, 203
Rhythm, alpha, 42 f.
Romans viii, 118
'Running down', of universe, 73, 159

Selection, natural, 106, 114, 118
Self, building of, 165

Self-consciousness, 121
Self-expression, 199
Senescence, 42, 44, 51
Simultaneity,
 eternal, 145–52, 160, 175, 185, 213
 temporal, 124–7, 130 f., 138
Sleep, 222
Solipsism, residual, 178
Soul, infusion of, 120
Space-time, 53, 132–8, 153–7
Spirit, of people, 189
Statistics, 62
Steady-state theories, 94, 97
Successiveness, 145, 149 f., 157, 165 f., 185
Suffering, 115, 118
Sundial, 48
Super-atom, 94
Super-nova, 95, 100
Survival, of fittest, 114
Symbols, 223
Synthesis, random, 111
System,
 closed, 61 n., 69, 73 f.
 living, 69 f.
 open, 69 ff.

Teacher-disciple relation, 200 f.
 in N.T., 203, 215
Teleology, 114, 121, 162
telos, 164 f.
Temporality,
 continuing, 166 f., 216, 222
 of created order, 158 f.
 taken up into eternal, 217 f., 222
Tension, within theology, 88 f., 99
Theology,
 biblical, 26–40, 141, 204 f.
 empirically based, 139, 155
Theories, revision of, 88
Thermodynamics, laws of, 60 f.

Time,
absolute, 17 f., 49
beginning of, 17, 73
biblical view of, 28–40, 141 f.
biological, 15, 42–7, 51
chronological, 30 ff., 38
dilatation of, 130 f.
direction of, 57 f., 63 f., 68, 70
extrapolated, 72–5
fiduciary, 178, 184
God's, 145
infinite, 21 f., 142 ff.
keeping, 51–5
linear, 34 ff., 39, 220
personal, 75 n., 221
psychological, 15, 42
public, 15, 18, 75 n.
realistic,, 30 ff.
relational, 72
reversal of, 56 f., 63
scales of, 15, 47–51, 144, 149
sense of, 15 f., 19, 41–7, 50 ff.,
66–71, 158
solar, 15, 48–52
subjective, Chap. III passim,
137 f.
theological status of, 159 f.
unit of, 53 f.
universal, 130 f., 153, 155, 158
Timelessness, 142, 145 f., 149 f.,
152 f., 186
Trial and error, 115, 118

Trinity, doctrine of, 155, 224
Truth, 20 f.
and falsehood, 103 f.
Turning-points, of history, 193

Understanding, mutual, 200,
202
Union, hypostatic, 208, 211
Uniqueness,
of Christ, 101
of man, 113
Universals, 207 f., 219
Universe,
age of, 71–5
expansion of, 93 f., 96 f.
models of, 91, 93 ff.

Validity,
of conceptual knowledge,
137 f., 154–7
theological, 140
Verification,
principle of, 103
scientific, 91, 108
Vertebrates, 113

Word, creative, 160 f., 213 f.
World-line, 135, 156 f., 161 f.,
197
World-point, 135, 156 f.
Worship, 223

GEORGE ALLEN & UNWIN LTD

London: 40 Museum Street, W.C.1
Auckland: P.O. Box 36013, Northcote Central, N.4
Bombay: 15 Graham Road, Ballard Estate, Bombay 1
Bridgetown: P.O. Box 222
Buenos Aires: Escritorio 454–459, Florida 165
Calcutta: 17 Chittaranjan Avenue, Calcutta 13
Cape Town: 68 Shortmarket Street
Hong Kong: 44 Mody Road, Kowloon
Ibadan: P.O. Box 62
Karachi: Karachi Chambers, McLeod Road
Madras: Mohan Mansions, 38c Mount Road, Madras 6
Mexico: Villalongin 32–10, Piso, Mexico 5, D.F.
Nairobi: P.O. Box 4536
New Delhi: 13–14 Asaf Ali Road, New Delhi 1
Ontario: 81 Curlew Drive, Don Mills
Philippines: 7 Waling-Waling Street, Roxas District,
Quezon City
São Paulo: Caixa Postal 8675
Singapore: 36c Prinsep Street, Singapore 7
Sydney: N.S.W.: Bradbury House, 55 York Street
Tokyo: 10 Kanda-Ogawamachi, 3-Chome, Chiyoda-Ku

BRITISH PHILOSOPHY IN THE MID-CENTURY

C. A. Mace, C. D. Broad, A. C. Ewing, S. Korner,
R. B. Braithwaite, A. Ambrose and M. Lazerowitz, H. Bondi,
A. J. Ayer, G. E. Moore, Gilbert Ryle, Stuart Hampshire,
Margaret Masterman, Theodore Redpath

British Philosophy in the Mid-Century is not only an authoritative review of some of the outstanding developments in British philosophy, it is also a significant contribution to these developments. The papers here published had their origin in a course of lectures at Cambridge arranged by the British Council, but many of the contributions have been revised and extended so as to present the latest views of the authors.

Of outstanding interest is a contribution written especially for this volume by G. E. Moore who has exercised so profound an influence not only on the theory of the subject with which this paper is concerned but also on the whole course of philosophical thought in Britain and elsewhere.

This new edition contains, in addition to 'postscripts' by many of the contributors, two papers on the philosophy of Ludwig Wittgenstein by Alice Ambrose and Morris Lazerowitz. The biographical and bibliographical notes on each contributor have been brought up to date.

Demy 8vo 35s. net

PHILOSOPHICAL ESSAYS

Bertrand Russell

This volume, is essentially a reprint of a book with the same title published in 1910. But because two essays in that volume have since been reprinted in *Mysticism and Logic*, they have been replaced by an article on history and another on Poincare's 'Science and Hypothesis'. Otherwise the essays stand exactly as originally published and the author has made no attempt to modify them to accord with changes in his opinions which have developed in the interval. The collection includes 'The Elements of Ethics'. 'Pragmatism', 'The Monistic Theory of Truth', 'James' Conception of Truth' and 'On the Nature of Truth and Falsehood'.

Demy 8vo 30s. net

GEORGE ALLEN & UNWIN LTD